This book belo~~ngs~~

Colin Lightfoot

THE SEA CHEST

Books by Captain Frank Knight

The Golden Monkey

Voyage to Bengal

Clippers to China

The Bluenose Pirate

He Sailed with Blackbeard

Captain Anson and the Treasure of Spain

Mudlarks and Mysteries

Family on the Tide

Stories of Famous Ships

The Young Drake

THE

SEA CHEST

Stories of Adventure at Sea

by Captain Frank Knight

ILLUSTRATED BY *William Riley*

PLATT & MUNK ✹ *Publishers* ✹ NEW YORK

Contents

CONTENTS

Illustrations

ILLUSTRATIONS

Foreword

by Harvey Swados

When I was a boy I dreamed of going to sea as a ship's surgeon. My father and my grandfather were doctors, and from the sea stories I had read and the motion pictures I had seen, it seemed to me it would be very grand to pace the deck of a great liner in a white uniform, traveling to foreign ports and occasionally saving someone's life with the aid of my medical skills.

But the fact was that I had no medical skills and lost the desire to acquire any. I never did lose the desire, though, to go to sea, even after I had decided during my college years to become a writer; and when the United States entered the Second World War, my opportunity came. After obtaining ordinary seaman's papers, I went on to a government radio school, and in the midst of the war I shipped out at last as a second assistant radio operator, a licensed officer on a Liberty ship bound for London through the North Atlantic with a cargo of bombs.

During the years that followed, sailing as everything from second assistant to chief, my ears were filled with wonderful stories told by my shipmates, ranging from skippers all the way down to the wipers in the engine room. We had some exciting experiences of our own, and some dangerous ones, too. Some of my closest friends were killed, one by an enemy torpedo, another by a robber's knife on the streets of Recife after he had survived the entire war.

But those of us who later left the sea for other pursuits had gained something we would never lose. A few of the adventures that were related to me as our ship glided through southern waters, or felt its way through the foggy Grand Banks, or tossed around in the stormy North Sea I later tried to write about, together with some of the experiences we lived through ourselves.

But there were many that I have never written about to this day, and Captain Knight's stories have reawakened my memories of them. There was for example the Kid, a boy of maybe nineteen, with a big mop of curly black hair—if I close my eyes I can see him now—who worked as a messman on our lazy tanker, heaving its way slowly across the Pacific. He told us one evening how he had been sitting just like we were on the taffrail of the last ship he'd been on, and how he'd fallen overboard, *splash!* just like that, also in the middle of the Pacific, with the nearest dot of land maybe a thousand miles away. "What happened?" we asked breathlessly. "Oh, I just paddled around," he replied nonchalantly, "and when the captain got word that I was overboard, he put the ship about, cursing a blue streak, and lowered a boat. It was a million to one shot, but they picked me up."

Well, if you want to find out what happened to young Pickering of the *S.S. Hopewell* in a similar emergency, read "Out of the Frying Pan," which has a very different ending.

Then there was a wild fellow whom we took aboard in Australia to deliver to the authorities in the United States for his infractions of naval regulations. Our skipper, a tough old bird himself, put the involuntary passenger to work in the galley walloping pots and pans. But one night this fellow ran amok, smashing all the crockery he could lay hands on, until it began to look as though all of us crew members would wind up eating with our fingers from the pots in which the food was cooked. The wild man had to be put in solitary, which meant that several of us had to catch him and then handcuff him to a stanchion, if we wanted to finish the voyage in peace and quiet, and with some dishes left.

Well, if you want to find out what happened to some other mutineers aboard another ship outbound from Australia over a hundred years ago, turn to Captain Knight's exciting story, "Australian Gold."

One thing I did learn from my long months at sea aboard various slow-moving ships, was that once you've acquired a taste for this kind of travel, it does get in your blood, and you will never lose it. Nothing can compare to the thrill of sighting land for the first time after a lengthy strenuous voyage, whether it be an island rising from the sea, a narrow estuary bordered with windmills, or a smoky bustling port—unless it is reading about it and dreaming about it, as Captain Knight offers you the chance to do in this book.

In the course of my fairly short period as a radio operator on merchant ships (which is better than being a tourist, because you get paid for it), I put in at such exotic ports as Benisaf in North Africa, Split in Yugoslavia, Loch Ewe in Scotland, Las Piedras in Venezuela, Pearl Harbor, Sydney, Brisbane. . . . And although it has been many years since I last shipped out, the salt has never dissolved in my bloodstream, and I know now that I will never have enough of travel to far-off places—or of traveling to them in ships. In recent years when I have had occasion to go to Europe, I have chosen an ocean liner over an airplane each time, and although to my mind being a passenger is a poor substitute for being an active crewman and feeling a close kinship to the vessel that rolls and pitches beneath your feet like a part of you, there is still that unbeatable thrill when the lines are cast off and you encounter the boundless vista of the heaving sea. And that shivery thrill of anticipation—so much better than simply being dropped from a nameless cloud to a distant airport just like the one you left behind—when your ship makes its way grandly to its berth in a seaport so different from the one you left behind that you feel you are entering a different world.

Let us hope that you and I will continue to have the opportunity in our lifetimes to roam the world as it has existed for the merchant seamen—varied, multifarious, with its wonderfully contrasting languages and costumes—before uniformity closes in upon it, as it is closing in upon so many other areas of our lives.

But if you are not yet ready to sail the seven seas you still can do it vicariously, for you have the opportunity to relive some of the most exciting days of the seafaring wanderers in the pages of Captain Knight's book which lies under your hand at this very moment.

Valley Cottage, New York
February, 1964

THE SEA CHEST

The Black Lugger

ICK BELLAMY saw the black lugger only once, and then faintly, for a minute or two on a dark night.

It was in the summer of 1720, and he had obtained permission from his father, who was the rector of the parish of Dean in Sussex, to go out all night with the fishing boats from Dean Gap. Only half a dozen small boats fished from the Gap, and all the men were known to Dick and his father. They were decent, honest simple men, living with their families in a cluster of tiny cottages by the Gap, selling their fish to the village people.

There was no moon that night, but the stars gave a little light so that the white chalk mass of Beachy Head was visible like a faint cloud. And it was against this mass that Dick suddenly saw the lugger.

He called out to the men in his boat—old Jess Durnford and young Jess, his son. "See—over there against Beachy! A big lugger!"

To his annoyance the men seemed suddenly intent on their net. They would not look.

"Jess! Quick, or she'll be gone! What is she?"

The lugger hauled her wind and seemed to pass very close to one of the Dean boats, though Dick could not see which one. He thought he saw a man in the boat stand up and take something from the larger vessel. Then the lugger's sails filled once more and she was gone, vanishing into the darkness toward Cuckmere Haven.

Old Jess Durnford looked up then, peering with narrowed eyes. "Where then, Master Dick? Where away?"

"Oh, she's gone now!" Dick snapped angrily. "You should have looked when I told you."

Old Jess shook his head. "Nay, Master Dick, 'twas your eyes playing tricks. 'Tain't safe to believe what 'ee sees at night." Young Jess chuckled, but said nothing.

Dick felt almost like hitting them. He knew these Sussex fishermen, and they could be as obstinate and irritating as mules if they chose.

For the rest of the night's fishing he refused to say any more about the black lugger, and even managed to forget her for awhile himself in the excitement of hauling the net and then racing the other boats home. But once the boats were beached it all came back to him.

Ned Bodley, one of the fishermen, produced from his boat a huge twist of coarse tobacco and began cutting it into lengths and dividing it up among the men.

Then Dick understood. "She was a smuggler!" he gasped. "You took that from her, Ned Bodley—I saw you!"

Some of them laughed, some muttered angrily and Ned Bodley demanded, "Why, 'tis no hanging matter, is it?"

"Yes," retorted Dick hotly, "it is! You know very well Sir John Lomax has vowed to hang any smugglers he catches! My father has always said there were none in Dean but he was wrong. I wish I had not come with you tonight!"

"Why then, will 'ee tell Sir John what 'ee've seen?"

"No," Dick snapped. "You know very well I won't. But what

am I to say if I am asked? Do you expect me to tell lies for you?"

They shuffled awkwardly at that, and presently he laughed at them angrily. "Oh, you fools! To run the risk of being hanged for the sake of an inch or two of tobacco! I thought Sussex men had more sense!"

Then he left them and set off toward home in the gray dawn light.

That was the root of the matter. Smuggling in itself seemed no great crime to him, but he did not want his friends to be hanged, and he did not want Sir John Lomax to triumph over them. Sir John Lomax was the squire and magistrate of the district, and not a very popular one.

Of course there was smuggling and smuggling. This kind did not seem wrong to him because it was so small. The men were buying tobacco for their own smoking, not to sell at a profit. But there were also big smuggling gangs who brought in tobacco and silks and brandy by the shipload and sold it on the London market. So far they had not been seen in the neighborhood of Dean, but where they operated they terrorized the countryside, stole horses to carry their goods, and even murdered people who refused to help them.

Dick's father had said once, "It is always the small men who are caught and hanged. The big men escape." And Dick remembered that now as he walked home.

He climbed the steep track from the Gap to the open Down. Ahead he could see the tower of the church and beyond that the great oak trees behind which lay the rectory garden. He did not mind going home through the churchyard, even at night. It joined his own garden and had always seemed almost a part of the garden. But he did object to passing the great Lomax monument which lay beyond the churchyard in its own ground, on the far side of the church from the rectory. The Lomax monument was like a monstrous Greek temple, with marble columns flanking the wide steps which led down to the Lomax family vaults.

Dick hated all this because it was pompous and new and to his mind spoiled the old gray church, and because Sir John Lomax had spent so much money on it while the cottages on his estate were allowed to fall into ruin for want of repair.

On a sudden impulse when he reached the church he decided to climb the tower. In a few minutes the sun would be rising. He had never watched a sunrise from the top of the tower. This seemed a good reason for doing it now.

He climbed on the outside, knowing the way up from childhood—first to the church roof, then to a narrow slot of a window in the tower, then to a drainpipe, from that to a stone gargoyle, and so over the battlements to the flat roof. And once there he paused to look around at the mist-covered countryside, the distant hazy sea, the trees and roofs of the village.

So he came at last to look down upon the Lomax monument— and the hairs of his head rose in horror. The great bronze door at the foot of the marble stairs, the door to the vault itself, was open!

All the stories that he had ever heard of ghosts and graves opening rushed upon him. He had always scoffed at them before —but not now! He had to grip the coping of the tower because his legs were trembling.

And then the door closed—apparently of its own accord. Nobody had appeared, either ghostly or living. The door was fast shut and solid as it had always been.

Dick did not wait to see the sunrise. He scrambled down from the tower and ran home through the churchyard and the rectory garden and did not stop till he was safe in the kitchen with Bess Parker, his father's housekeeper, who was kindling the embers of the fire for the day's cooking.

"Why, bless me, and I was thinking you were fast asleep in bed like your father! And you're all of a shake, too! What ails ye, boy? Have ye taken a fever?"

"No," he said breathlessly, feeling rather ashamed of himself now. "I—I've been running. I'm going up to bed now!"

"Oh dearie, dearie—what with your father sitting half the night over his books and you running out with those fisherfolk. . . ."

He left her still complaining, and went upstairs.

Once in his bedroom, with the sun rising at last, he was sure that he must have imagined it all. The door could not have been open! What had old Jess said? *'Tain't safe to believe what 'ee sees at night.* Yes, that was right. It hadn't been completely dark at that hour, but still too dark to see distinctly. He *must* have imagined it.

And with this comforting thought he fell asleep.

Dick's mother had been dead some years. Bess Parker managed the house and had brought him up as well as she could. Dick's father was always so busy, with a widely scattered parish to attend to and books to read and write, that sometimes Dick saw almost nothing of him from one week's end to another.

The week following Dick's fishing excursion was one of those times. Dick had been wanting to tell his father about the smuggled tobacco, so that he could speak to the fishermen and try to persuade them not to run foolish risks. But three days passed before he managed to find an opportunity.

Then one morning he saw his father's library door open, and his father standing by the window. Dick rushed in.

"Father, did you know that Jess Durnford and the others were smuggling tobacco . . . ?" And with that he stopped suddenly. He could have bitten his tongue out, for seated in the room and a little behind the door was a young soldier—he had coughed while Dick was speaking.

"My son Richard," said his father dryly. "Captain Lambert, Dick, of the regiment stationed at Lewes. Captain Lambert is to be our guest for a week or two."

"Our—our guest, Father?"

"That is what I said. Some of his men will be quartered in the village, and the captain will stay here. He will have the room next to yours. And now, you had some ridiculous story about smuggling?"

"N-no, Father," Dick stammered. "It—it was nothing!"

His father frowned. "Please do not make it seem even more ridiculous than it is. I heard, and the captain heard. As it happens I had just been assuring him that our fishermen do not indulge in smuggling. Now you say they do. You put me in an awkward position, boy."

Dick thought unhappily that he himself was in a far more awkward position. What could he say?

And then, while he stammered and hesitated, he was saved by the captain rising to his feet and saying, "Mr. Bellamy, you must excuse me. I have to see to my men. Perhaps I may hear the story at some other time."

Dick blessed him silently. When he had gone he could talk to his father more freely.

His father listened to the story, then said, "I am not surprised you did not wish the captain to hear it. I thought it was some rumor or gossip you had heard in the village. As it is, I'm afraid it confirms what Sir John Lomax has already told the captain."

"Sir John Lomax!"

"Yes—but I am sure he had no evidence, otherwise he would have had the men arrested. He merely told the captain that he had his suspicions and advised him to keep watch on the Dean Gap men. Well, I will do what I can with them, but you know how obstinate they are."

"I do!" said Dick grimly. "But what will you tell the captain, Father?"

His father considered that for a moment, then said, "I think we should tell him of the black lugger. You are sure you saw her, Dick?"

"Quite sure, Father."

"Then that is the ship for which the soldiers should be watching. I shall try to persuade the captain of that, and try to shield our men as much as possible. I think our men have merely been weak, and perhaps the captain will agree with me. He seems a reasonable kind of man."

Dick agreed with that. It had been very reasonable indeed of the captain to leave the room just then. Therefore he was not unduly worried when, a day or two later, he met the captain walking alone in the churchyard.

"Ah, Dick, I have been admiring your father's church. A charming building in charming surroundings, but somewhat spoiled, I fear, by yonder monstrosity." And he waved a hand toward the Lomax monument.

Dick grinned. "We think so too, sir."

"Do you? I am glad of it. It shows you have good taste. And your taste in fishermen, Dick—is that as good?"

Dick stared at him. "I—I don't understand!"

Captain Lambert smiled. "I mean, Dick, that I hope your father is right and Sir John Lomax is wrong. I hope your friends of Dean Gap are really honest fishermen and not smugglers."

"Oh!" Dick exclaimed—and then, eagerly, "They are, sir! I know they don't mean any harm by their smuggling. It was only a little tobacco for themselves. And if—if you could catch the black lugger they wouldn't be able to get it!"

But at that the captain looked at him closely and asked sharply, "The black lugger? What is she?"

Dick gasped and stammered again. "I—I thought my father had told you about her, or I wouldn't have said——"

"But you should have, Dick. No doubt your father meant to tell me, but I have scarcely seen him since our first meeting. You must tell me now."

And his manner was so quiet, his blue eyes so friendly, that Dick did.

When he had finished the captain murmured, "Cuckmere, you think. Yet she was a big vessel. Would she find water enough in the river?"

"I think she would then, sir, for the tide would have been full within an hour."

"Ah—a moonless night and a full tide. And when, Dick, would you expect those two conditions to operate together again?"

"Why sir, it happens about every four weeks—that would make it a day or so more than three weeks from now." Then Dick asked eagerly, "Do you mean you will set a watch for her?"

"Aye, perhaps. But Dick, I must swear you to secrecy. Not a word to your father even, and especially not a word to your friends the fishermen."

"But, sir, may I not even warn them to have nothing to do with the lugger?"

"Not even that. For you see, Dick, though they may be your friends, they must also have friends aboard the lugger. They would pass on the warning."

"But—they may be arrested with the others. Sir John Lomax would hang them if they were brought before him!"

The soldier shook his head. "You must trust me, Dick. We are after bigger game than your friends at the Gap. Help me and I will do what I can to help them. Tell me of anything you hear or see—anything that may have a bearing on the black lugger or the men who own her."

And Dick promised. He felt that he could indeed trust the young soldier.

But, though he tried to think of something, there was nothing else he could tell the captain then. It had been on the tip of his tongue once to tell him how he had imagined he had seen the door of the Lomax vault open that morning—but now he was quite ashamed of himself for having given way to panic over such an absurd flight of imagination. He would not tell anyone about that!

And as the days passed he heard nothing and saw nothing, even though he spent two more nights out with the boats. It was all very disappointing. The soldiers were in the village, doing nothing except an occasional drill on the Downs, a formal march to church on Sundays, and a very informal walking-out with the village girls in the evenings.

The captain seemed to have forgotten all about smugglers. When he was not drilling his men he spent much of his time visiting at Dean Hall, the stately home of Sir John Lomax, or riding one of Sir John's horses on the Downs.

Then one afternoon, almost four weeks after Dick had seen the black lugger, everything changed.

Dick was asking his father's permission to go out that night with the boats. His father always gave it, but Dick knew better than not to ask. Captain Lambert was sitting in the room with them, reading. And on this occasion it was he who suddenly raised his head and said, "No!"

Dick stared at him. So did his father. The captain apologized.

"I beg your pardon, sir. It is not my place to interfere. But— there are reasons why Dick should not go out with the boats tonight."

"Indeed, Captain? What reasons?"

"Reasons which I cannot disclose to you, Mr. Bellamy. Reasons which are His Majesty's affair and not mine."

And suddenly Dick knew! That night the black lugger might come!

The captain was pacing the room now and seemed agitated. Dick's father was frowning. And abruptly the captain said, "I will tell you this much, sir, in absolute confidence. Sir John Lomax has heard—I do not know how—that a smuggling run may be made at Dean Gap tonight. He has ordered me there with my men. I cannot refuse."

The rector groaned. "I wish you had not told me. I can only pray it is not true."

Dick cried, "It is not true! I don't believe it! I—I shall go and tell Jess Durnford!"

He was darting from the room, but the captain sprang at him and held him.

"Dick, remember your promise!"

"I don't care! Father, tell him to let me go!"

"Mr. Bellamy—in the King's name!"

Dick's father groaned again. "Dick—I must keep the side of law and order, and so must you. You must not go."

"I shall go! I don't care what anyone says!"

"Dick, go to your room!"

"No! I—oh, let me go!"

But struggling was useless. Those strong arms held him more firmly than ever. And presently, with the rector's consent, Captain Lambert carried Dick to his bedroom and locked him in. It was no comfort that he should whisper as he did so, "Dick, don't be an idiot. Trust me."

Dick could not trust him any longer. He saw now that he and the captain were on opposite sides. The captain was acting under the orders of Sir John Lomax, and could not save the fishermen even if he wished to.

Dick lay on his bed and tried to think. And after awhile the answer came to him. He must wait his chance. He could act in darkness, but not now. So he lay still and waited, watching the sun go down and the daylight fading. Not until it was dark did he make a move.

He could almost laugh now. Did they really think they could keep him in? Why, he knew the way down from his bedroom window as well as he knew the way down from the church tower!

He opened the window noiselessly, swung his leg over the sill, felt with his toes for a ledge of stone below it, then swung the other leg out. A foot or two to the right of the sill, his toes on the stone ledge—a square iron drainpipe with brackets at intervals of four or five feet, a thick stem of ivy for additional support, and then his feet touched the ground.

He did not know the time, but he thought that if he ran all the way he might get down to the Gap before the soldiers could close in. They would not do so until the boats were out.

Dick thought that even if the boats had gone he would find some means of getting to them. There would be a skiff or a dinghy on the beach. He would take that and row out to them. If he could not he would stand on the beach and shout as they came in, and so ruin the ambush. The main thing was to get to the Gap before the soldiers.

He slipped through the garden and over the wall into the churchyard. He ran through that and out at the far gate onto the open Downs. He could see the edge of the cliffs now—a black undulating line against the purple sky—but little else. And suddenly it occurred to him that if he ran past the steep lane which led to the Gap, came down to the cliff beyond it and scrambled down to the beach and so came back to the Gap that way, he would avoid the soldiers if they were on the Downs ahead of him.

So he kept away from the cliffs for the present, as though he were making for Cuckmere rather than Dean Gap. Sometimes he stumbled, sometimes he tripped over brambles, but still he ran. Suddenly, as he turned to dodge a clump of blackberry bushes seen at the last moment, a pair of arms reached up, caught his legs, and he pitched headlong.

"Got you, my hearty!" said a rough voice with satisfaction.

Then Captain Lambert's voice called softly, "What is it, Sergeant?"

"A varmint of a boy, sir! Hold quiet, blast you! Ah, bite me, would you!"

Then the captain came, stooped and exclaimed, "Dick! Lud, boy, could ye not trust me that far?"

Struggling in the sergeant's arms Dick panted, "No! You

will do what Sir John tells you! I—I meant to get down to the Gap——"

"The Gap, Dick? You are past the Gap now. Had you lost your way?"

"No. I was going down to the beach. . . ." And then Dick stopped, realizing that the soldiers were also past the Gap. Had they lost their way, then?

"Let him go, Sergeant," said the captain quietly, and took Dick's arm himself. "Now come with me, Dick lad. I want to talk to you."

He led Dick away out of earshot from the men. "Sit down now, or our figures may be seen against the skyline. Now Dick, listen to me. We are not going to the Gap at all."

"Not to the Gap? But you said Sir John had ordered you——"

"Never mind Sir John. I told you we were after bigger game than your Dean Gap fishermen, and you should have believed me. Why do you think we are on the Cuckmere road?"

"The black lugger!" Dick gasped. "You mean you hope to find her in Cuckmere Haven?"

"We shall not, but a sloop-of-war is lying in wait for her off Beachy Head. We are here to take her cargo if she manages to land it. What she may land in Dean Gap is nothing. The major part has another destination—London."

"But—there is no road to London this way!"

"There is, for smuggled goods. Did you think they would be carried to Lewes and thence by the high road? No, I am convinced they come over the Downs to some hiding place for the first night, and from there are taken by night to other hiding places, until they reach London by some devious way. But enough of that now. It is the cargo I want, and perhaps some of the men with it, though I suspect the most important men behind it are safe in their beds at this moment. My chief worry is that I cannot watch the whole Downs from one place, and if

I spread the men out too far I shall not have them at hand if they are wanted."

"I could help you watch!" cried Dick eagerly. "I'm sorry that I didn't understand, and—and I want to help now. If you would let me——"

"Aye—but how could you help?"

"The church tower, sir! If I kept watch up there, I could see the whole line of the cliffs from Beachy to Cuckmere, and up the valley too. If I saw men coming over the edge against the skyline——"

"Why, so you might! But more than men, Dick—a great string of packhorses is what you must look for. You would scarcely see men. And even horses you might mistake for bushes or trees. Look for movement, Dick—any movement, any little change in the shape of the skyline. That will be your warning. And then you must warn us. Can you hoot like an owl? Three little hoots, Dick, a short interval between the first and second, and longer between the second and third. Can you do that?"

Dick did it softly to show him—"*Tu-whit, tu-who—tu-who-o!*"

The captain laughed. "Excellent! Run then—but do not become impatient. Nothing may happen for hours. Nothing may happen at all. And don't fall from the tower in your excitement!"

Dick laughed at that, then sprang up and ran back the way he had come. And presently he was crouching on the roof of the church tower high above the world, peering out across the country through the battlements.

And now he realized why the captain had warned him against impatience. The entire countryside was silent and still. It was impossible to believe that a lugger might be running over from France, while a warship lay in wait for her, that soldiers lay hidden out there among the blackberries, and that presently there might be fighting in the darkness.

He watched the stars moving slowly overhead. He wondered when the moon was due to rise, or if the sun would rise before it did. As yet there was not even a glimmering of dawn to be seen. All the sky was a rich dark purple, with only the stars to break it.

Dick could see the line of the cliffs clearly enough against the sky, but of the churchyard immediately below him he could see little—just the faint shape of a stone monument here and there, and the Lomax imitation Greek temple like a hazy cloud. He was glad he could not see that in greater detail.

But suddenly, as he was staring in that direction he realized that he could see more of the tomb than before. He stared, his eyes big and round with horror, for a narrow vertical shaft of light had appeared below the Greek temple, and as he watched it widened.

The door to the vaults was opening! There was light within the vault!

He was too terrified even to scream. He crouched, frozen to the coping of the tower. And then for an instant he glimpsed the figure of a man standing in the doorway. It disappeared and slowly the light went out, fading as though it were moving back deeper into the vault. Finally it disappeared, but he knew the door remained open.

Dick forgot smugglers, forgot the call of the owl. As soon as his limbs would move he was over the battlements and scrambling down over the church roof. When he reached the ground he ran wildly across the Downs toward where he had left the soldiers.

He found one by falling over him. The man cursed and grabbed him. And as before Captain Lambert's voice immediately demanded, "What is it? Who is it this time?"

"Captain Lambert! Captain Lambert! The tomb! I saw the door open and there was a light inside!"

"Lud, boy, are you mad? What are you gibbering about?"

Dick tried to calm himself and talk sensibly. "It's true, sir! I was looking toward the Lomax monument, and I saw a light!

The door opened—and there was a man! I—I lost my nerve and ran."

And then, to his surprise, the captain uttered a low whistle and exclaimed, "By Jove, the tomb! I had forgotten that! Sergeant! Sergeant Coggs—come here to me!"

"Aye, Captain, coming! Blast my eyes if it isn't that boy again!"

"Never mind the boy. Sergeant, we must alter our plan. The boy's sharp eyes have given us a great chance. But wait! Dick, back to your tower! Never mind the ghosts—they will not hurt you! Watch for those horses, boy. You will see them soon enough now, I'll warrant. And give the call. Do nothing else, mind! Even if you think we have not heard do nothing else! Do you understand?"

"Yes, sir, but——"

"I will have no buts! You have your orders. Go!"

And Dick went. He knew now what it was like to be a soldier. Orders were orders! And once more upon the tower, though he was uncomfortably conscious of the Lomax monument with its open door behind him, he would not look toward it. He stared instead at the skyline of the Downs over toward Cuckmere.

The captain had been right. He had not long to wait. Presently he saw what seemed no more than a little hump grow in the line of the Downs against the sky, and the hump seemed to wriggle.

Tense with excitement, he steadied himself and gave the signal. *"Tu-whit, tu-who—tu-who-o!"* And after he had waited a full minute with his heart in his mouth, it was answered in the same way.

And after that he could only watch the hump and wait.

He could see nothing of the soldiers. Once he thought he heard a rattle of metal on stone and a muttered curse, then the gruff undertone of a man's voice. But apart from that there

was only silence and darkness, until presently he heard the un-
mistakable sound of horses shaking their bridles.

The hump had long since disappeared. Whatever it was had
melted into the general darkness. Then Dick saw horses begin
to breast the rise from Cuckmere, and emerge onto the level of
the Downs. Now they were approaching the church.

They were almost beneath him before he saw them clearly—
twenty, twenty-four—why, there must be nearly thirty! And all
were swelled to a monstrous size by the packs on their backs
and hanging at their sides. Men, a dozen or more, marched beside them, leading them in strings.

They skirted the churchyard, keeping to the wooded side opposite the rectory and the village, and made directly for the
separate ground by the Lomax monument. And suddenly, as he
looked in that direction, Dick saw the light reappear and
heard a man growl something—a cloaked figure who stood
holding a lantern at the foot of the marble steps.

Dick was not frightened now. There were no ghosts here—
only living men and horses.

The horses were halted. At once the men began unstrapping
their loads. A man went down the steps of the tomb with what
was clearly a small barrel on his shoulder. Another followed.
They entered the vault, disappeared for a moment, and came
out empty-handed.

The process went on almost in silence save for the champing
of the horses. Dick, almost hopping with anguish on the tower,
had to bite his tongue to prevent himself from crying out. Where
was the captain? Would he never act?

And then, when most of the load must have been conveyed
below ground, there was a sudden shout, "At 'em, lads!"

It was as though the earth had exploded. Soldiers sprang
into being out of nothing. Men dropped barrels, cursed, and
turned to fight or run. Horses reared and screamed. A figure
dropped from the Greek temple clean down to the doorway of

. . . there was a sudden shout, "At 'em, lads!" It was as though the earth had exploded. Soldiers sprang into being out of nothing. Men dropped barrels, cursed, and turned to fight or run.

the vault upon the cloaked man with the lantern. A naked
sword showed for a moment in his hand. And then the light
went out.

Now Dick could see nothing—only hear the shouting, the
blows, the clash of steel and wood and stone. Yelling at the top
of his voice himself, though he did not realize he was doing it,
he swarmed over the coping and scrambled down the tower.
By the time he reached the ground the noise was already dying
down.

And before he could reach the scene of the fight he caught
a glimpse of another lantern bobbing through the churchyard
and he heard his father's voice calling, "What is happening?
Who is there? Thieves! Robbers!"

Dick took the more sensible course and ran to him. "Father!
It's all right! It's the soldiers!"

"Dick! What are you doing here? Soldiers? What do you
mean, boy?"

"Captain Lambert's soldiers have captured a lot of smugglers
—with horses and hundreds of barrels of brandy! They were
putting it all in the Lomax vaults!"

"In the——? Nonsense, boy! Captain! Captain Lambert!
Good heavens, sir, that's Sir John Lomax!"

It was. The lantern held high showed the figure of the
baronet, his cloak thrust away, lying full length on the ground
with Sergeant Coggs seated on his chest.

Captain Lambert, somewhat disheveled and mopping his brow,
came up the steps from the tomb. "Well, sir, that was hot work!
But we have them all, I think, and one or two wounded. May
we take them to the rectory?"

"Yes, but—man, what is the meaning of it all?"

The captain smiled wearily. "Why, it's plain, is it not? This
Greek temple of a tomb covered one of the resting places for
contraband goods which we had been seeking. Sir John Lomax,
the magistrate who would hang all smugglers, was one of the

chiefs himself. And your Dean fishermen—why, they were no more than decoys."

"Decoys, sir?"

"Aye. Given a trifle of tobacco to bring them into the game and keep their mouths shut. And when it suited Sir John here he set me against them to cover the main activity, hoping that I should waste my time with them and go away contented. Fortunately, with Dick's help, I did not fall into the trap."

"With Dick's help? Why, what could the boy do?"

"Oh, a great deal, I assure you. You shall have the full yarn later. But I can tell you Dick is a great catcher of smugglers— though not of ghosts, eh, Dick?"

"N-no, sir," Dick muttered, and wondered if he would ever be able to live that down. But then he grinned and said, "You see, sir, I didn't know the spirits were in barrels!"

The *Hopewell's* Tiger

AND THAT," the shipping agent in Bombay informed the *S.S. Hopewell's* chief officer, "completes your cargo—except for the tiger."

The chief officer blinked. "Er—did you say *tiger?*" he inquired doubtfully.

The shipping agent grinned. "I did. Didn't you know? You're taking it across to Ormuz for the Sultan's private zoo. It's rather valuable, so look after it."

The chief officer's face slowly assumed that purple hue so well known to his cadets and junior officers. He made a visible effort to keep his voice calm, and failed. "And where," he demanded in rising tones, "do you suppose I am to stow a tiger? In my cabin? Or will it sleep with the men? And if you think I am going to feed it with chunks of meat on the end of a stick . . ."

The agent patted his shoulder soothingly. "It'll be in a cage—a sort of cage, anyway. We'll just hoist it on deck, and you'll

35

hardly know it's there, except that you'd better rig an awning to keep the sun off it. Tigers like a bit of shade, you know. As to feeding it, there'll be a keeper to do that—a fellow called Mahmoud."

"Never in all my days—!" the chief officer exploded, but paused to gape at a truck rumbling its way along the pier. On the truck was a huge wooden crate. And in the crate, glaring out between its slats, was a tiger.

The crew of the *Hopewell* also paused to stare. They lined the rail to watch their unusual passenger come aboard.

"Just a big cat," explained Jim Roberts, better known as Slim, among the cadets, because of his plump, well-fed look. "Quite harmless if it's treated properly. Puss, puss!"

The tiger looked at him and licked its lips.

"Don't tease it," said White. "It's sheer cruelty for anyone as fat and juicy as you are, to show off in front of it. Go and hide in the cabin."

The giant hook of a dockside crane swooped down on the crate, grabbed its wire slings, swung it high in the air, and dropped it with a nerve-shattering bump on the *Hopewell's* deck.

Even tigers have nerves. This one proved it by roaring madly, then hurling itself backward and forward against the sides of the crate. The crate lurched and creaked.

"Get it lashed down!" the chief officer shouted to the crew. "Go on—it can't get out!"

The men were not so sure. It could get one paw out, and it seemed to have a very long reach. They advanced with coils of rope as gingerly as elderly ladies venturing onto an escalator.

Then a tall, bearded, brown-skinned man wearing a turban and very little else arrived carrying a joint of meat big enough to make a meal for the *Hopewell's* entire crew of forty.

"Here's Mahmoud," said the shipping agent. "He'll show you how to handle the beast."

The demonstration was not impressive. Mahmoud darted in, opened a hatchway in the side of the crate, thrust the meat in, slammed the hatch shut and darted back just as an outstretched paw tried to grab him. The tiger pounced on the meat, but was obviously annoyed at having missed Mahmoud. However, while its attention was on the meat the crew were able to secure the lashings.

"They'll hold, whatever happens," said the chief officer. "I only wish I felt as certain about the crate."

"Oh, that's all right," said the shipping agent, who was not traveling in the ship. "Three days and you'll be there—if the fine weather holds."

"If!" grumbled the chief officer. "Why in blazes can't people be content with the animals in their own countries?"

However, for the first day the weather did remain fine. The old *Hopewell* pushed her way steadily across the Arabian Sea. The tiger panted in the heat beneath its awning and only roused itself to roar at feeding time.

"That's natural," said Roberts. "All animals make a noise when they're hungry. You'll notice it with dogs, cats, babies——"

"And even certain cadets eclept Slim," put in young Pickering. "The row you make when a meal happens to be a minute or two late! Ouch—you clumsy brute!"

Roberts, pouring himself a fourth cup of tea, had let the stream from the teapot stray onto Pickering's knee.

"Sorry. The ship rolled." He said it casually, and then looked up, suddenly alert, and repeated it in tones of awe. "You know, that's right! *The ship rolled!*"

They stared at him. He had of course been out in the sun. But abruptly his meaning dawned on them. If bad weather was coming—what about the tiger?

Through the open door of their cabin they watched the sea. It was gray and ominous. It was heaving like a bad-tempered giant awaking from sleep. And from aft came a sound of complaint, something between a howl and a roar. The tiger did not like the look of things either.

They went along to look at it. The tiger greeted them with a sad moan. A wisp of spray blew over the rail and hit the tiger in the face. It snarled, shook itself, and backed against the far side of the crate. The side of the crate bent. Another wisp of spray came and the tiger plunged wildly. The crate shuddered in every joint.

"It's not good for him," said Roberts. "He'll hurt himself."

"It's not good for the crate," said White. "That's more important. Come on, Slim—we'll get that awning off and rig it as a screen to keep the spray off. Pickles, nip along and tell the chief officer what we're doing."

The new arrangement had little effect. The tiger lay behind the screen and moaned.

"He's seasick," said the chief officer. "Poor beast—I felt that way myself on my first trip to sea. Oh well, it'll keep him quiet."

But as darkness came, the rolling of the ship increased. Seasick or not, the tiger roared his disapproval. And since he always stood up to roar just at the wrong moment he was almost always thrown off his feet and hurled against the side of his crate right in the middle of the roll.

The thing developed into a regular rhythm. *Roll—roar— crash!* It became monotonous. The crew of the *Hopewell* became used to it and forgot it. One can become used to anything.

Nevertheless the chief officer issued special instructions for the night. To the second and third mates he said, "Send a cadet along to have a look at the beast every hour." To the cadets he said, "If you see any sign of the crate breaking up tell the officer of the watch at once."

"And what," the second mate asked sarcastically, "is the officer of the watch supposed to do then?"

"Oh, you'll think of something," the chief officer replied

easily. "It's surprising how even a dull brain will react to an emergency. Good night!"

Young Pickering had the first watch, with the third mate. At nine o'clock the tiger was lying down and whining. At ten o'clock he was being sick. At eleven o'clock, evidently feeling better for it, he was standing up on his hind legs trying to see over the canvas screen. At midnight, when Pickering and Roberts went along to view him together, he greeted them with a hopeful roar.

"There you are," said Pickering, "he's been sick and now he's hungry again. I tell you it's the sight of you, Slim. His mouth is watering."

"I'm not awake enough yet to think of a suitable reply," Roberts muttered. "I'm not awake enough to see the crate properly, either. Isn't it sort of bent?"

"That's the squint in your eyes," said Pickering, who was feeling happy because the watch was over and he could turn in.

Roberts let him go and went up to the bridge. He did not tell the second mate he thought the crate looked bent. The second mate had also only just left his bunk and would probably also make some withering remark.

For an hour Roberts listened to the tiger protesting about the rolling of the ship. At one o'clock he went aft to look again, and after that he did tell the second mate.

"There's something funny about the joints at the top," he said. "At least, not funny, but queer. I can't see it properly in the dark. . . ."

"Then take my flashlight and make sure," snapped the second mate. "What's the use of saying you *think,* and there *might* be, and you're not sure, but perhaps. . . . Oh, go away, you make me tired!"

"Yes, sir," said Roberts, and went away. On his way down the ladder it occurred to him that the tiger was quiet now for the first time since midnight, and had, perhaps, gone to sleep.

Halfway along the deck he thought he saw something ahead that ought not to be there—like an engine room ventilator in the wrong place. He switched on the flashlight. Something *was* in the wrong place, certainly, but not a ventilator. It was the tiger.

Afterward Roberts boasted of how he kept his head at that moment, how he remembered to keep still and how he saw at once that the tiger was frightened of the glare from his flashlight.

The truth was that he was petrified. He was too scared to yell, run or switch off the flashlight—which was just as well because the tiger *was* in fact frightened of it.

A moment later the tiger disappeared.

For one hopeful second Roberts tried to persuade himself he had imagined it. Then, by the rays of the flashlight, he saw a fluttering rag of canvas that had once been a canvas screen, and beyond that the crate, looking decidedly more than bent.

The horrible truth came to him suddenly. He was alone on the afterdeck with a hungry tiger—a tiger he could no longer see.

He did yell then—a bloodcurdling yell which must have frightened the tiger as much as it frightened the second mate on the bridge. It also frightened the chief engineer, who woke abruptly thinking his engines had given up the ghost at last. But by the time the chief engineer could switch on his light, Roberts was on the bridge.

"I tell you I did see it, sir! It was sitting waiting for me! It looked—horrible!" And Roberts shuddered at the memory.

"Well, where is it now?" demanded the second mate. "Where did it go? What's the use of coming and telling me——Raow!"

This, as he leaped around at the sound of a soft footfall. It was not the tiger, however. It was the captain in slippers and pajamas.

"What on earth is the meaning of all this noise? I thought I heard a scream!"

"It's the tiger, sir——"

He switched on the flashlight. Something was in the wrong place, certainly, but not a ventilator. It was the tiger.

"The tiger screaming? Nonsense!"

"No, sir. That was Roberts. The tiger's loose, sir."

"Loose? Do you mean loose? Good heavens, man, do you mean *loose?*"

"That's what I said, sir. On the afterdeck somewhere. Roberts saw it and then it vanished. I told him he should have———"

"Of course he should! How could it vanish? Tigers don't vanish. They—Holy snakes!"

Roberts had never seen anything like it. One moment the captain was there, the next moment he was not. Nor was the second mate. The chartroom door had slammed behind one, the wheelhouse door behind the other.

And a moment after that Roberts was not there either. At the top of the ladder on the starboard side of the bridge two yellow-green eyes were balefully glaring. Roberts went down the ladder on the port side without touching it.

The chief officer was in his bunk dreaming that at last his merits had been recognized and he had command of a ship. From this pleasant dream he was aroused by that wretched cadet Roberts, shaking him and gasping, "Tiger! Tiger!"

It took a full minute for the chief officer to realize that he was in fact in command for the present of the *S.S. Hopewell.* At least, he was in command as far as he could be with a tiger in charge on the bridge. At any rate the captain was locked in the chartroom, so someone had better do something.

"Call all hands," he said firmly. "Switch on every light you can find. I want the ship flooded with light—understand? We've got to trap the brute. And get that fellow Mahmoud up here. It's his job—not mine!"

That was a comforting thought, but not so comforting in practice. Mahmoud, when it was at last made clear to him that the tiger was free, uttered a prayer in Hindustani and disappeared. Twelve hours later he was found deep in the bowels of the ship with the anchor cable.

Roberts roused the other cadets first. Then the three of them went around the ship together because it was safer that way. Even so they could only look in three directions at once, and they had an uncomfortable feeling that the tiger might be lurking in the fourth direction. Of course he might be still on the bridge, but he might not.

The chief officer called a conference in the officers' mess-room. He shut the door in case the tiger decided to join in.

"First thing is to get the crate mended," he said. "It's not much use trapping the brute if we've nowhere to put him. That's the carpenter's job, except that the engineers had better help with some steel brackets or something. We don't want it breaking up again."

The chief engineer said he could attend to that. The thing was, how were they going to trap the beast?

"In a cargo net," said the chief officer. "We'll rig it across one bridge ladder and drive him down into it somehow. I've seen pictures of wild animals being caught in nets."

"Maybe you have," said the chief engineer, "but how are you going to drive him into it? That's what I want to know."

"What about the hose, sir?" White asked. "He hates water. If we could take a hose up one ladder and give him a good dousing I'll bet he'd dive down the opposite ladder like no-body's business!"

The chief officer beamed. "Excellent! With plenty of force on the pump—yes, we'll do it!"

It all took time. Both cargo nets and hose were stowed away and had to be brought on deck. There were arguments as to how the net had better be rigged so that the tiger could not escape.

When they were almost ready, with the hose pointing up the port ladder, the cargo net around the starboard ladder, and men standing by with flashlights at all strategic points, the chief officer heard a door banging down below.

It was a sound which always roused him to fury. Doors could be shut, or they could be hooked back. They must *not* be allowed to swing and bang when the ship rolled.

"Some fool," he roared angrily, "has left a door banging. White, go down and see to it."

White went and came back grinning.

"Well, whose was it?"

"Yours, sir. I've shut it."

The chief officer glared at him and seized the hose. "Now, follow close behind me with the flashlight. Stand by to close the net, there! Ready? All right, turn on the water!"

The jet shot up the ladder. The chief officer pushed the nozzle of the hose before him and turned it across the bridge.

For one moment it seemed as though the operation had been immediately successful. From the bridge there came a howl of dismay. From the starboard ladder came a shout of triumph as something plunged down into the net and the net was drawn tight.

Second thoughts changed opinions. That howl had been human, not tigerish. And the fugitive caught in the net was wearing pajamas and slippers.

It all took a good deal of explaining. The second mate, who had met the full force of the jet just as he was emerging from the wheelhouse, was almost speechless. The captain, who had avoided the water but found the net, was quite speechless.

Worst of all, the tiger was not there. Apparently he had spent an hour ranging from the wheelhouse door to the chartroom and back. Then, giving up hope, he had vanished. Nobody knew where. Probably he had gone down one of the ladders just before the trap was ready.

Men shivered and looked over their shoulders. Those who had flashlights shone them into dark corners. But there were many dark corners and few flashlights. Having a tiger loose on board ship is bad. Not knowing where he is, is worse.

The chief officer sighed. At least he was no longer in command. "What do you suggest, sir?" he asked the captain.

"Tcha!" snapped the captain, rubbing his bruises. "Find the brute, of course! Get your beastly net rigged somewhere else! Don't stand there asking fool questions!"

The chief officer sighed again. There was a lot of injustice in the world, he felt. And he, he supposed, would have to lead one of the search parties.

"Tiger hunting!" young Pickering snorted. "Those chaps in India don't know anything, doing it with elephants and guns and hundreds of yelling beaters! They ought to try it this way."

They crept around the ship in little groups, shining flashlights and carrying sticks, ready for action. It was not good for the nerves. Once something touched Roberts' leg and he was halfway up the mainmast rigging before he realized it was the carpenter's jacket hanging on the rail where he had been working. The boatswain, crawling on all fours to peer around a hatchway, met a young seaman crawling around the same hatchway in the opposite direction and received a smart crack on the head from a stick before he was recognized. The third mate suddenly shouted, "Take that, you brute!" and broke his stick over a cargo winch.

Then dawn came and men could at least see each other. But still they could not see the tiger.

"He must have gone overboard," said White. "We've looked everywhere!"

"Poor beast," sighed Roberts. "I wonder if he can swim?"

"There'll be the devil to pay when we reach Ormuz," the chief officer muttered. "That animal was valuable."

"I wash my hands of all responsibility," declared the captain. "Why you could not have seen that the crate was weak I don't know! It seems I must do everything myself on this ship!"

The chief officer snorted. There were times when he felt like telling the captain the whole truth and nothing but the truth, and this was one of them. However, he swallowed the impulse and barked at Roberts instead.

"I'm going to the bridge to relieve the second mate. Go to my cabin and get my jacket—and don't stand there like an idiot."

That made Roberts indignant. After all, his watch had ended long ago. He ought to be in bed. White was on watch now.

In fact White fully agreed with him. He followed Roberts, and they arrived at the chief officer's cabin together. White flung the door open. Roberts took half a step inside—and stopped. He gave a choking cry and fell back into White's arms, pulling the door shut with a bang after him.

"The tiger," he gasped weakly. "I saw it. It's in there. Oh, my sainted aunt!"

They gazed at one another in horror. They tiptoed around to the outside of the cabin and peered in at a porthole.

It looked like a tigerskin rug, sprawled out across the cabin. But it was breathing, and it had been sick again. Also it was surrounded by chewed books, torn clothes, half-eaten shoes, and the springs and other interior arrangements of a mattress. It opened one eye as they watched it, and quite distinctly winked.

They crept back to the door. White turned the key in the lock. Then, taking the key with them, they silently went up to the bridge.

White held out the key. "You'd better have it, sir. I've locked the door just in case."

The chief officer gaped at him. "Just in case what? What on earth do you mean? Where's my jacket?"

"Just in case someone went in and didn't notice, sir. You see, the tiger's in there."

It was terrible, seeing a strong man shattered like that. Roberts felt sorry for him for the first time in his life. His face became so purple it seemed impossible that he did not burst. Roberts sighed and slid down the ladder. Better go quietly to bed, he thought.

Nobody, not even the captain, dared speak to the chief officer for the rest of the day. Everyone avoided him and tried not to look in his direction, as they might with a man who had suffered a great sorrow. The second mate, forgiving him his wetting with the hose, silently allowed him to share his cabin. The captain just as silently lent him a spare jacket. The steward brought him ice water with his meals. And they hoped he would not see Mahmoud poking lumps of raw meat to the tiger through the cabin porthole.

Next day the ship arrived at Ormuz. A radio warning had been sent ahead, and as the ship anchored off the little white town a barge arrived carrying Arab zoo keepers with nets and ropes especially designed for catching tigers. Within an hour it was safely netted. Roaring angrily and taking with it the remains of the chief officer's rugs and his best uniform, it was towed out and pushed into the crate. Still roaring, it was swung overboard into the barge. When last seen by the crew of the *Hopewell* it was spitting out brass buttons from the chief officer's best coat.

It was not the last they were to hear of it, however. In the afternoon a white and chromium launch zoomed up to the ship, bearing the Sultan himself. He was fat—much fatter even than Roberts. He beamed on all and sundry, showing very white teeth. He held out his hand with a load of gold rings for the captain to kiss, but said in perfect English that he had really come to see the chief officer.

And on that astonished officer's breast—or rather on the borrowed jacket which covered it—the Sultan pinned a large silver medal with a green ribbon above it.

"The most Honorable Order of the Silver Grasshopper," he

said, beaming more than ever. "It is for taking such care of my new tiger. Much have I heard of British ships, but never have I known a chief officer who would give up his own cabin to a tiger! Always—always in future shall this ship carry my tigers for me!"

He turned and bounced his way back down the gangway. It was just as well, for the chief officer's face was turning purple again and he was making rumbling noises under his breath.

The Sailor of the *Sussex*

THIS IS A TRUE STORY. It is the story of an ordinary seaman who lived about two hundred years ago—no great admiral or famous voyager, but just one young man among fifty or so who signed aboard the East India Company's merchant ship *Sussex* as foremast hands for a voyage to China and back in the year 1736. His name was John Dean.

In those days the outward voyage to China might take anything up to a year. The East India Company's ships never hurried, preferring safety of ships and cargoes and comfort of passengers to mere speed. In any case they were heavily built ships, and generally deeply loaded with valuable cargo. "Make haste slowly" was their motto.

The outward voyage was accomplished by the *Sussex* without serious accident. There would have been the usual call at Madeira to take wine on board. A call might be made at the Cape of Good Hope, or at Madagascar or some smaller island near it off the east coast of Africa, to refill the water casks,

obtain fresh fruit and vegetables, and carry out whatever repairs might be necessary. Another call might be made at
Ceylon, or perhaps cargo taken to Madras and discharged.

It all took many, many weeks, but nobody worried, and at last
the *Sussex* would find herself anchored off Whampoa, near
Canton, surrounded by Chinese boats bringing the silks, tea and
rhubarb she was to take to England.

It may seem strange that rhubarb should be mentioned, but
in those days it was much used by doctors as a medicine, and
it grew nowhere but in China. An emperor of China once said,
"The English people live on tea and rhubarb. One could easily
defeat them in war by stopping their supplies of those com-
modities."

So the *Sussex* loaded her cargo, about five hundred tons and
worth in those days a considerable fortune. And she sailed for
home in company with the *Winchester,* another East India Company's ship. It was wise to sail in company, for pirates swarmed
in the East Indies. All the East India Company's ships carried
guns, and two of them together might prove a match for even
a man-of-war.

About half the voyage home was completed peacefully
enough, and the crews must have thought the worst of their
troubles over when the longitude of the Cape of Good Hope
was once more reached. This was in the early part of 1738—
and then the two ships ran into bad weather.

Cape of Storms, the early Portuguese sailors had called the
Cape of Good Hope, and so it proved for the *Sussex* and *Winchester.* For weeks they battled against westerly gales, and by
the time they were over the *Sussex* was almost a wreck. She had
lost both main and mizzen masts and was leaking badly. She
was still afloat, but only just.

The pumps were set to work. A new foresail was set on the
one remaining mast. The *Winchester,* not so badly damaged,
stood by. For a while it seemed as though the battered *Sussex*

might at least be able to make port in some civilized country, if not to reach England. And then her master, Captain William Gostlin, lost heart and decided to abandon ship.

Probably he feared the *Winchester* would sail on and leave him. There was still the whole of the South Atlantic Ocean ahead, and the North Atlantic beyond that. Some seven thousand miles of water lay between him and England. Another severe gale would almost certainly sink the leaking ship. He consulted his officers, and they agreed with him. They had better abandon the ship and transfer to the *Winchester* while they had the chance. It was the ordinary seamen, John Dean and the rest, who disagreed.

This may seem strange to us, especially since both captain and officers had shares in the cargo and stood to lose a lot of money by abandoning it. But the fact is the seamen stood to lose a great deal more—their whole wages for the two-year voyage.

Wages were then paid only for a completed voyage. If the ship did not get home, no matter for what reason, the seamen were not paid at all. She might be sunk, wrecked, captured by an enemy, or lost in any way through no fault at all of the crew; but the crew, if they managed to struggle home, were the losers. They might have been away years—and in those days they would not be paid any "advance of wages" during the voyage—but still they got nothing unless the voyage was completed.

That was why John Dean and the rest protested against the decision to abandon the *Sussex*. Thirty of them refused point blank to leave the ship. She would float, they said, long enough to get her ashore somewhere. They would repair her leaking bottom, make new masts for her and set up new rigging. Only give them the chance.

Captain Gostlin was an obstinate man. It infuriated him that common seamen should dispute his orders. He ordered them again to go on board the *Winchester*. Again they refused. So he and his officers smashed the *Sussex's* longboat with axes.

It was the only boat big enough to hold all thirty men. If they remained aboard the *Sussex* now, and she sank under them, they would have no chance of escape. Only the tiny pinnace remained to them, scarcely capable of holding half their number.

It was a harsh argument, and it impressed some of them. Fourteen of the thirty gave in and went on board the *Winchester*. John Dean with fifteen others refused to abandon ship.

Gostlin went almost mad with rage. He and his officers and those men who dared not defy him rushed about the crippled *Sussex* doing as much damage to her as they could. They smashed her equipment, took away her navigation instruments and portable gear, even tried to cut down the new foresail. When the men who insisted on remaining in spite of all this asked him at least to tell them their latitude and longitude, he absolutely refused. And at last he and his party crossed to the *Winchester,* and she sailed away.

The *Sussex* was left, adrift, leaking and disabled, in the midst of unknown waters with only sixteen determined heroes on board her. And not one of them knew anything about navigation.

They repaired the foresail, rigged such other temporary sails as they could, and let the ship drift eastward before the westerly wind. They worked at the pumps until they were ready to drop. And the wind, by pure chance, carried them to Madagascar— a wild, uncivilized land, but land of some sort. They managed to beach the ship in St. Augustine's Bay.

For three weeks John Dean and his companions worked as few seamen would be able today. They careened the ship— rigging blocks and tackles to trees and heaving the ship over on her side so that they could repair her bottom. They felled trees to make new spars for her. They sewed canvas and spliced ropes to make new sails and rigging for her. And at last they considered the ship seaworthy.

They put to sea, and their optimism must have been as great as their obstinacy. Sixteen men to do the work of a hundred;

sixteen men to trundle around the mighty capstan where normally four dozen labored; sixteen men to hoist the massive yards,
set and tend the great sails, steer, pump, keep watches at night,
and do all the thousand and one jobs necessary on a ship without
any mechanical power to aid them. And not one of them was a
navigator.

However, they set out, knowing that if they could work the
ship across the Mozambique Channel they would find the coast
of Africa. If they could follow that southward and westward
they would come to the Cape of Good Hope, and that would
bring them into the Atlantic.

And then, with all their optimism and bravery, disaster defeated them. On the second day out the ship struck the Bassas de
India shoal in the Mozambique Channel. She was utterly
wrecked.

Somehow the men managed to launch the little pinnace. They
had no boat davits; the pinnace would be stowed on deck,
probably on one of the hatches. She would be lifted over the
side with tackle rigged from one of the yards and lowered into
the surf breaking over the shoal.

Sixteen men swarmed into the tiny craft. In the rough water
she promptly turned turtle and eleven of them were either
drowned or crushed to death against the wreck.

The remaining five, with John Dean among them, managed
to right the boat and scramble into her. Without food or water,
without oars, rudder or sail, they drifted in her for seventeen
days until finally she threw them up once more on the shores
of Madagascar.

They were utterly exhausted, starving, some of them injured
or raging with fever. One by one four of them gave up the
struggle for life and died. Only John Dean remained at last, and
he had been found by natives and taken into slavery by a local
chieftain.

For many months Dean served as a slave to his black master,

Sixteen men swarmed into the tiny craft. In the rough water she promptly turned turtle and eleven of them were either drowned or crushed to death against the wreck.

but his services must have been well appreciated, for in July 1739, more than a year after the *Sussex* had been abandoned, he was sent on a mission to the coast of the island. There, at the mouth of the River Manarivo, he was overjoyed to see an East India Company's ship, the *Prince William,* sheltering in the roadstead.

Even then, however, his troubles were not over. He managed to present himself on shore to the captain of the ship, but the captain at first refused to have anything to do with him. He may have thought Dean to be a deserter, or perhaps a stranded pirate—at all events a bad character who would only cause trouble on board his ship. One bad character among a crew might easily be the cause of mutiny.

John Dean for a while struggled desperately between two forces—the servants of his black master who were insisting that he return inland with them, and the captain of the East India-man who refused to listen to him. But at last he succeeded. He escaped from the chieftain's officers, swam out to the *Prince William,* and persuaded her captain to believe him.

Unfortunately the *Prince William* was then outward bound, not homeward. Almost two years were yet to pass before John Dean would reach England. He had first to make another voyage out to India and China. But the captain, now impressed by Dean's story, wrote it all down and sent a copy home to the directors of the East India Company, putting the letter aboard a homeward bound ship or leaving it at Madagascar to be collected by the next homeward bound ship calling there.

When John Dean did reach England—in 1741, about five years after leaving it aboard the *Sussex*—he found himself quite an important man and in the midst of much excitement. Captain Gostlin and his officers were in trouble.

The letter from the captain of the *Prince William* had reached the directors in 1740. They promptly sent for Gostlin and other officers and questioned them. Not satisfied with the replies re-

ceived, the directors set up a court of inquiry. And as a result
of that, and John Dean's evidence, they sued Gostlin at law for
the loss of the cargo. For almost two years the suit was argued
in the courts, but in 1743 the East India Company won. Gostlin
had to pay £25,000—an amount equal to about £200,000
or $560,000 today. A shipping company could scarcely hope to
recover such a sum of money from a captain nowadays, but the
captains of the old East Indiamen were wealthy men, having
substantial shares in the cargoes they carried and often in the
ships they commanded. A captain could make a fortune in three
voyages and retire.

So Gostlin was punished and John Dean rewarded—a result
which did not often happen in those days when the common
seaman was regarded as little better than an animal.

In November, 1743, John Dean was granted a pension of
£200 a year for life, the equivalent of $4,480 today, and £50,
or $1,120 a year to his wife should she survive him. The direc-
tors also gave him an immediate present of fifty guineas, or
$250, and a little later made him head porter at one of their
warehouses. These were handsome rewards indeed to a poor
sailor, and far more generous than he would ever have received
from the Royal Navy. But the East India Company was always
generous to its servants.

As a crowning touch to this unusual story of a poor sailor
amply rewarded, the directors had John Dean's portrait painted
by a famous Dutch artist. It hangs in a London museum today,
among hundreds of portraits of distinguished people, a tribute
to the pluck and determination of *un*common seaman John
Dean.

The *Flying Dutchman*

THE *Flying Dutchman* was only a ghost ship, no matter how many old sailors claimed to have seen her. The American schooner *Governor Parr* was real, however—but in her way just as much of a ghost.

In 1921 she was found adrift in the Atlantic, rigged, sound, loaded with cargo, but without anyone on board. A tanker towed her into port.

Two years later she was adrift again, still sound, but once more without a soul on board. Again she was taken in tow, but this time she broke away and went off by herself. She became a danger on the Atlantic. Ships were warned to look out for her. Coast guard vessels went in search of her. After a month or two she was found, set on fire, and left to burn herself to ashes. A month or so after that she was seen again, still afloat, with no fire damage visible!

For almost a year she haunted the Atlantic shipping routes. She was seen again and again, sometimes moving toward North America, sometimes toward Europe. But always she had vanished by the time a coast guard or naval vessel could arrive with intent to sink her.

Not until late in 1924 did she finally vanish—the phantom derelict of the Atlantic, the liner captain's nightmare!

Captain of the Pork

MR. MIDSHIPMAN Thomas Lorimer lay sprawled at full length on the deck of *H.M.S. Bombard,* sixty-four-gun ship of the line. The ship was cruising in leisurely fashion on the Spanish Mediterranean coast, hoping that some French or Spanish warship would appear and put up a fight. Failing that, she was prepared to pick up any French or Spanish merchant ships which might venture out.

Mr. Midshipman Lorimer was writing a letter to his mother.

My dearest Mother,

This does not leave me in any very good frame of mind. Yesterday I was sent ashore with the cutter to fill water casks. We beached the boat in a small river where the shore was very muddy. In carrying the casks to and fro the men naturally brought much mud into the boat. I intended to set them to clean it out after we returned to the ship. However, when I returned the first lieutenant ordered me to some other duty, and the men left the boat as it was. An hour later the first lieutenant saw it and had the audacity to inform me I was only fit to command a *pigsty*. This I considered very unfair—

But at that point Mr. Midshipman Lorimer stopped writing, stuffed the letter and his writing materials quickly in the portable case his mother had given him when he left home, and ran to one of the gunports.

An astonishing sound had reached his ears—a sound like the screeching of a hundred souls in torment.

He was not the only one to be astonished. Everywhere men rushed to the ship's side. The watch below came tumbling up on deck. Men in the tops and out on the massive yards stood and gaped. And the only thing to be seen was a small, ungainly, dilapidated Spanish coasting vessel, her sails patched and baggy, her hull low in the water. The sound seemed to be coming from below her battered decks.

Some men, in addition to gaping, began to mutter uneasily. An Irish seaman hastily crossed himself and moaned, "Save us, if the Devil himself's not come afloat!"

Another man exclaimed, "They're cutting the throats of poor prisoners on board! That's what they're doing, to stop us taking them alive!"

And one was of the opinion the crew of the Spanish vessel must be suffering from some peculiar form of madness which caused them to scream in agony.

Mr. Midshipman Lorimer did not believe any of these explanations. On the other hand he had no sensible alternative to offer.

And then he heard the first lieutenant barking orders and the skirl of the boatswain's pipe. The cutter was being ordered away, and he was supposed to be in charge of it. He ran to the upper deck and presented himself, ready to face the Devil or a crew of madmen if need be.

The ship lay under backed topsails as the cutter was put over her side. The second lieutenant entered the cutter as boarding officer, bringing a small party of marines. Tom Lorimer gave the

An astonishing sound had reached his ears. . . . Everywhere men rushed to the ship's side.

orders—"Let go! Shove off, bow! Give way, all!" The boat leaped forward as the men strained at their oars.

They pulled around the coaster cautiously. Two or three men on her deck stood waiting for them, and they were evidently neither madmen nor devils. But as the cutter pulled around to leeward another factor arose—a most appalling smell.

"Faugh!" the second lieutenant gasped. "Get around to windward of her again—quickly, before we're all poisoned!"

"You—you mean to board her, sir?" Tom Lorimer asked doubtfully.

"I don't know. I'll give her a hail first. Let's see if they can understand my French. It's bad, but my Spanish is worse."

"Ahoy! What have you got on board? I mean—*Qu'est-ce-que vous avez pour* cargo?—What's the French for cargo, Lorimer?—Oh, *marchandise!*"

They understood at all events. Back came the answer in a single Spanish word which every man in the cutter knew.

"Puercos!"

"Pigs!" The men gaped at each other again and began to laugh. Pigs! Why had nobody thought of that?

"Put me aboard," the second lieutenant growled. "Pigs! Oh, help, what a prize to take!"

Mr. Midshipman Lorimer took the cutter alongside the coaster, but his thoughts were gloomy. That stench—and the first lieutenant had said he was fit only to command a pigsty! The insult had not really come home to him until now. And now they were alongside, the smell was unavoidable.

Ten minutes later the cutter was on her way back to the ship, however. The second lieutenant was taking the skipper of the coaster on board for questioning. His Spanish was not good enough, and the squealing pigs made conversation additionally difficult. Four marines were left on board the coaster as guard, much to their disgust.

The seamen in the cutter laughed at them heartlessly, but it was not long before they were even more disgusted.

Mr. Midshipman Lorimer, waiting for orders in the cutter, was startled to be commanded to report to the captain on deck.

"Mr. Lorimer," the captain demanded, looking him up and down, "have you sufficient navigation to take yon prize to Gibraltar?"

Tom Lorimer gasped. "Why, yes, sir—I think so!"

"*Think* is not enough! Can you or can't you?"

"Yes, sir, I can!"

"Very well, then. Take four seamen from your cutter's crew. You will not need more. Send the marines back on board here and allow the Spaniards to go ashore in their small boat. The cutter can tow them to within a mile or so of the beach. Report to the captain of the port when you reach Gibraltar, and request him to provide a passage for you and the men to rejoin us as soon as convenient. We shall be with Admiral Nelson's squadron off Toulon. Is that clear?"

"Yes, sir."

"Away with you, then. Oh, one moment . . ."

"Yes, sir?"

"A cargo of pigs seems something of a joke to you, no doubt. Am I right?"

"N-no, sir. I—I had not thought of them as a joke!"

"Good, for I can assure you, they are not. They are as valuable, almost, as gold and silver. For ships and armies need food, Mr. Lorimer, and pigs are very excellent food. Therefore, rather than let them fall into the hands of the French, you are to sink the prize. I wish that to be clearly understood. If the pigs cannot be brought to Gibraltar, they must not be brought anywhere."

"Very well, sir. I shall remember that."

"Right. And good luck."

"Thank you, sir."

And when he stood at last on the deck of his first real command, Mr. Midshipman Lorimer felt that he would need good luck. Gibraltar was a hundred miles away. The old coaster was making about two knots in the present slight breeze, but if she made any more, if the breeze strengthened at all, he was fairly sure she would fall to pieces.

Still, a first command is a first command, and even an elderly tub full of pigs is an important command to a boy of sixteen. In spite of the squealing and the smell Tom Lorimer would not have changed places with any midshipman in the Navy at the moment.

He watched the sails of the *Bombard* sink below the horizon. He watched the Spanish shore fading from sight as he set course somewhat to the southward from it.

Then he was alone with his unpleasant cargo, with night coming on and nearly a hundred miles of open sea ahead and an enemy coast only just out of sight. He was glad of the company of his four tough seamen.

He divided the men into two watches, two men to sleep and two to stay on deck. The two men due to turn in elected to sleep on deck. So did Tom Lorimer, giving orders that he was to be called at once if the wind changed or anything else happened. The pigs also seemed to have gone to sleep. At any rate, they had stopped squealing.

At midnight one of the men called him. "Wind's freshening from the eastward, sir. Bit of a sea getting up, too."

The old ship was pitching heavily. Her timbers groaned with the effort and her mainmast was creaking ominously. The pigs were squealing again.

"All hands on deck," said Tom above the racket. "We'll take a reef in everything, Dawson. Mainsail first, to relieve the strain on the mast."

"Aye aye, sir! All hands, there! Tumble up and reef sail!"

All hands were on deck anyhow, and awake. It was not long

before the patched sails were reefed. After that the ship seemed more comfortable, but she was still driving hard and making a good four knots.

One of the men muttered, "Pigs is seasick, sir. Poor beggars!"

"How do you know?" Tom inquired. "Have you been down to look?"

"Yes, sir. Couldn't abide 'em squealing like that."

"You're a braver man than I am, Smith!"

"No, sir—only my father keeps pigs back in England. I was brought up with 'em, so to speak."

And then Dawson came aft with the more serious news. "There's two feet of water in the lower hold, sir. I thought I heard it swishing about, so I took soundings."

"Hum . . ." said Tom. "All right, sound it again in half an hour and see if it's increasing. And have a look at the pump."

Tom was steering now, though the massive tiller was at times almost too much for him to hold with the wallowing sea causing the rudder to kick from side to side.

At about two o'clock in the morning Dawson reported again. "Nearly three feet in the hold now, sir. Reckon she's making water fast."

Tom whistled. "All right. What about the pump?"

"A bit shaky, sir, but seems to work."

"Very well. Call all hands."

"We're here, sir," the voices of the other two men growled.

"Good. You heard what Dawson said, then. She's making water fast, but the pump seems to work. Do we try to keep her afloat, or do we run for the beach and give ourselves up as prisoners of war?"

The men laughed. "We'll pump, sir."

"You realize we have no boat to escape with if she should sink under us?"

"Aye, sir. But—beg pardon, sir."

"Well, Larkin?"

"There's four big empty barrels on deck for'ard. If we caulked them they'd maybe keep us afloat if the ship did sink under us."

"A good idea! All right, watch on deck, caulk barrels and see that they float off if the ship sinks. Get some ropes around them, too, for lifelines. Watch below, man the pump. At eight bells change about, and after that every hour. Go to it, then!"

"Aye," growled the man Smith, "but what about the pigs if she sinks?"

"We'll give them a chance to swim ashore if we can. But if we get them to Gibraltar they'll be killed anyway. Perhaps they'd prefer to drown."

Smith shook his head. "No, sir. Begging your pardon, sir, but pigs is born to be killed, not drowned. Drowning's no death for a pig, sir."

Tom laughed. "Nor for us, I hope, Smith!"

Smith went off shaking his head and muttering, "Sailors is born to be drowned. Pigs isn't. 'Tain't natural."

At four o'clock Dawson reported, "Three feet still, sir. Pump's just keeping level with it!"

"Very well. Change the watches as I instructed."

Tom was striving hard to keep calm and to sound calm. The men were behaving magnificently, but one sign that he was losing his head might throw them into panic.

The four big barrels were standing ready and seemed reasonably watertight now. With ropes around them and the ends trailing, men might cling to them for hours. There were only four barrels for five men, of course, but that could not be helped. If the ship sank there might be other wreckage—hatch covers and spars, for instance.

He had made up his mind that if the ship did sink the men must have the barrels. He, as the officer and commander, must take his chance. So must the pigs.

But he let one of the men take the tiller for him now. It had almost pulled his arms out of their sockets, and his ribs were bruised and agonizingly sore.

At five o'clock he calculated that the ship must have run about thirty-five miles since leaving the *Bombard*. About one-third of the distance to Gibraltar.

At the same time the water in the hold was reported to be three feet four inches. The leaks were gaining on the pump. But the sails were drawing well; the masts and gear were miraculously holding. The ship was driving fast before the strong easterly wind.

Daylight came. The sun rose. The horizon showed clear and empty. Neither ship nor shore could be seen.

At eight o'clock Tom took a sight of the sun with his sextant and calculated the longitude with the aid of his pocket watch. It showed that the ship had been traveling even faster than he had estimated. Only forty-five miles now separated her from the longitude of Gibraltar. But a pocket watch is no chronometer, and Tom knew well enough that his longitude could not be called reliable. Still, it gave cause for hope, and he passed the information on to the men.

"If this breeze holds we should make port by sunset. Keep at it, lads!"

And at that moment the pump jammed.

Dawson said quietly, "Four feet of water now, sir."

"Very well. Dismantle that pump as quickly as you can. It may only be choked with weed."

Then one of the men had another brilliant idea.

"Seems a pity to see them barrels doing no good, sir. Couldn't we lash 'em alongside? They might keep her afloat."

Tom considered that. They were big enough, certainly. But of course they would take the speed off her, and they might not be available for saving life if required.

"Very well," he said. "Leave the pump for the moment. All hands to it. Lash them securely now, as far down the hull as you can, and two on each side. All right, Smith—I'll take the tiller."

It was a major operation, and the little vessel's gear was not in good condition for hoisting heavy weights over the side. It took an hour for each barrel: to rig tackle and hoist it—each was as tall as a man and as big around as four men—lower it over the side and secure it, then shift the tackle for the next barrel.

It was midday before they were finished, and by that time they were all practically exhausted. But they were picked seamen, and the job was well done.

Dawson reported five feet of water in the hold. At the same time Smith said sadly, "Pigs is nearly up to their flanks in water when she rolls, sir."

The hold was in fact only a little over four feet deep. The water was above the level of the 'tween decks where the pigs were tethered. But the ship was still afloat, and might now remain afloat even if her bottom planking opened right up. Those barrels ought to hold anything.

On the other hand the wind had dropped. With that and the dragging effect of the barrels the ship was scarcely moving. Tom ordered the reefs to be shaken out of the sails, and after that estimated her speed as little more than two knots. Gibraltar seemed as far away as ever.

There was another problem—that of food and fresh water. The *Bombard* had left them with a bag of salt beef and another of biscuits. There were a few beans and onions in the crew's cabin, on which the Spaniards had apparently existed, but they had not been intending to sail as far as Gibraltar. There was one cask of water, and nothing at all for the pigs.

"Oh, well," Tom sighed to himself, "if the worst comes I shall have to order Smith to kill a pig, I suppose. I wonder if he'll object to that? They're almost his pets now!"

There was also the certainty that all hands would have to get some sleep during the coming night. They had had almost none the previous night and had been working hard for many hours.

Two hours later they had the pump cleared and working. But the depth of that water in the hold remained at five feet. Tom looked over the side and saw that the barrels were more than half-submerged. They were bearing the weight of the ship. She could not sink any lower unless they also leaked or the lashings gave way.

With the breeze fallen and the sails requiring no attention he revised the order of watches. One man could keep the pump going easily; one man could take the tiller. The other two could sleep for an hour. He himself dropped down on deck where he was and in an instant fell fast asleep.

And then, at four o'clock, a hand was on his shoulder and a voice was saying in his ear, "Sail dead astern, sir. Coming up fast."

Tom jumped up and rubbed his eyes. The vessel appeared to be a brigantine. As her hull rose above the horizon a row of gunports became visible. And as she drew near she was seen to be flying French colors.

"A privateer!" he exclaimed. "Of all the luck!" Then he cried angrily, "Confound it, she's almost in British waters! Oh for a frigate to come out from Gibraltar to teach her a lesson!"

But there was no frigate, no other sail of any kind, and obviously no escape for Tom's first command either.

He forced himself to think quickly. Could he pretend to be Spanish? It was impossible. He could speak scarcely a word of the language, and his men were so obviously British that they would give the game away immediately.

Fighting was out of the question. There were five of them, with a total of four muskets, one pistol, four cutlasses and one dirk between them. Against them they would probably have a hundred men, well-armed, plus the brigantine with her twenty or more big guns. One cannonball would sink the little coaster. One volley of small shot might kill her entire crew.

He sighed and told the men, "We haven't a hope. We shall have to surrender, but we need not be ashamed of doing it."

The men sadly agreed with him. There was nothing else to be done.

The brigantine reduced sail as she came abeam of the coaster. A boat could be seen ready for lowering. But it was not lowered. Something seemed to be puzzling the Frenchmen—and suddenly Tom Lorimer realized that the pigs were squealing again. He had become so used to their noise that he had long ago given up taking any notice of it. The same applied to the smell. Noise and smells scarcely mattered by comparison with other troubles.

But now he did take notice, and he remembered how both noise and smell had worried him when he first encountered them. He remembered the men talking about ghosts and devils and madmen.

A man jumped into the brigantine's mizzen rigging and raised a speaking trumpet. A voice called, in French, "What is that noise there?"

Tom answered in English. "Our passengers! They are very sick and frightened. We are trying to take them to Gibraltar, but our ship is sinking!"

The voice replied in English, and seemed startled. "You are English! What make you in a Spanish vessel?"

"I told you!" Tom shouted back. "We are taking sick passengers to Gibraltar. They are very sick. They scream all day. Can you send a surgeon to us?"

That last was a piece of cool cheek. If they did send a surgeon it would be the end of everything. But he guessed they would not, and he guessed right.

"No! We have no surgeon to spare for English pigs!"

One of the seamen chuckled softly, and Tom bade him sharply be silent.

"They're moving down to leeward," another man muttered.

"They're bound to get the smell in a minute or two."

And they did. Men could be seen holding their noses or covering their mouths with handkerchiefs. Hastily an order was shouted, and the brigantine bore up to the wind.

"They're sheering off!" a seaman cried gleefully. "You've tricked 'em, sir!"

"Silence!" Tom snapped. "If they see you grinning they'll catch on." And he raised his voice and shouted in a tone of utter despair, "But our ship is sinking! See, we are only floating on barrels! Please take us on board!"

"No," came the reply. "Drown, English pigs!"

"Now—shout, all of you!" Tom muttered to the men, and set the example himself. "Help! He-elp!"

It was realistic—four men and a boy wailing and a cargo of pigs shrieking, for the pigs responded almost as though they, too, were obeying Tom's order.

Its only effect was to make the privateer crowd on more sail to get clear as soon as possible.

And at last Tom and his crew relaxed, though the pigs did not. The men collapsed on deck, laughing and holding their sides. Tom felt suddenly weak and dropped down on the cabin top. If the Frenchmen could still see them they must have thought they had collapsed through despair.

"Thank heaven she was only a privateer!" Tom exclaimed presently. "A regular man-of-war would not have been so easily fooled! But privateers are only out for profit, and a cargo of plague-ridden passengers cannot be very tempting. Back to the pump, lads—and pray for a sight of Gibraltar in the morning."

And when daylight came, after another night of toil and anxiety and snatches of broken sleep, there was the great rock of Gibraltar towering up to greet them, with the matching hills of Ceuta on the African coast.

"Navigation—and luck!" Tom breathed with relief. "And not a single passenger dead yet, eh Smith?"

"No, sir," Smith replied sadly. "But thin, sir, very thin. I don't reckon my father would give much for 'em in market, now."

"Well, we shall see how the garrison will welcome them presently," said Tom. "If fresh meat is as scarce as it was when I was last ashore there I think they will not complain that we have starved our passengers."

And they did not complain. As the shabby little coaster drifted into harbor, scarcely moving through the water and barely afloat at all, she was first boarded and then taken in tow and beached by a naval pinnace, and soon Tom found himself being congratulated on all sides.

"Excellent piece of work, Mr. Lorimer! Your admiral shall hear of it!"

"A most welcome cargo, my dear sir! The Governor will be delighted!"

And two days later Mr. Midshipman Thomas Lorimer, sprawled at full length on the lower deck of a frigate, was once more writing to his mother.

My dearest Mother,

This leaves me in a considerably better frame of mind than when I last wrote to you—but since my last letter is still in my writing case you will not have received it. I have now to inform you that I have just completed my first voyage in command, and as a result was invited to dine with His Excellency the Governor. The principal dish was roast pork. As I had, in a manner of speaking, supplied the pork, His Excellency was pleased to bestow on me a new title—"Captain of the Pork." But of this more when I see you. For the present I am on my way to join Lord Nelson off Toulon, where he and I together will, I trust, be more than a match for the French and Spanish admirals.

Your loving son,
Tom.

Eight Bells

QUESTION: When will you hear sixteen bells struck on board ship? *Answer:* Just once a year—at midnight on New Year's Eve. Eight bells are struck to mark the end of the old year, and eight for the beginning of the new.

Eight bells are in fact struck to mark the end of each four-hour watch throughout the day and night; that is, one bell for each half-hour of the watch. And the strokes always come in pairs for each completed hour—*ding-dong—ding-dong—ding-dong—ding-dong.*

There are six watches, but the evening one is divided into two "dog watches" of two hours each. Nobody knows why they are called dog watches, but someone has suggested it is because they are "curtailed!" Their purpose is to give the two watches of seamen a change of hours. Thus a watch coming on deck at midnight would work until four a.m., come on deck again from eight a.m. until noon, then again from four p.m. until *six* p.m., and then again from eight p.m. until midnight, when it would go below until four a.m. and so work through the following day in the alternate watches.

The first watch is from eight p.m. till midnight. The middle is from midnight till four a.m. The morning watch follows, and the forenoon watch is from eight to noon, with the afternoon from noon till four p.m.

The second dog watch, six to eight p.m., is traditionally the one in which the crew can amuse themselves by singing, etc. But eight o'clock means "silence and lights out," and woe betide anyone who makes a noise after that!

Out of the Frying Pan

It was a sweltering hot night. There were storms around, but somehow the *S.S. Hopewell* had missed them. Even now, as she made her leisurely way through an oily sea around the northern verge of the Bahama Islands and into the Florida Straits, there was lightning in the distance and the remote rolling of thunder.

At midnight young Pickering went onto the bridge to relieve Roberts. "The cabin's like an oven," he grumbled. "I haven't slept a wink."

Roberts knew that was not true because he had just spent ten minutes trying to wake Pickering. However, it was too hot to argue.

"The whole ship's like a frying pan," he said. "I think I'll drag my mattress out on deck somewhere." And he added as an afterthought, "That's Turtle Cay light flashing over there, by the way." Then he went below.

He did drag his mattress out, but he did not immediately lie down on it. The thought suddenly occurred to him that he would enjoy a cigarette.

Now this was a new accomplishment of Roberts's, and he was rather bashful about it. The others were inclined to make unkind jokes about it, such as standing by him with a fire extinguisher ready, so he preferred to do his somewhat experimental smoking in private.

On this occasion he went right aft, perched himself on the poop rail, lit a cigarette, and sat puffing contentedly and watching Turtle Cay light winking away to port.

And then the light went out.

Roberts was startled. Lights in lighthouses didn't vanish just like that. He jerked around to see what had happened to it, wobbled, grabbed at the rail and burned his bare knee with his cigarette, gasped, and went overboard, too startled even to shout as he fell.

In fact, it all happened so suddenly that he was several fathoms deep before he realized it.

When he did reach the surface again the ship's sternlight was a mere pinpoint of light, rapidly fading. And though he shouted, then, it continued to fade.

For a few seconds he gave way to panic—yelled wildly, splashed, swallowed gallons, and tried to swim after the ship. But then he pulled himself together and took stock of his position.

Obviously it could have been a lot worse. He was a good swimmer. He was wearing only shorts and vest. The sea was calm and warm. And there was Turtle Cay, not much more than a mile to the south. He could not see it, but he took direction from the North Star and began to swim.

Perhaps an hour later his feet touched sand. Exhausted, he crawled from the water, staggered up the beach until the sand felt dry, flung himself down, and fell asleep.

On the *Hopewell's* bridge the second mate also noticed that Turtle Cay light had gone out. He waited a few minutes to see if it would come on again, then went around to the radio cabin to rouse the wireless operator.

"Sorry to disturb your beauty sleep, Sparks, but you'd better get a message through to Nassau. Turtle Cay light has just gone out. Darned dangerous, when you come to think of it. You'd better warn any ships following us to give the reefs a wide berth."

Young Pickering did not go down to the cadets' cabin until a quarter to four, when it was time to call Jumbo White. He saw that Roberts's bunk was empty, and said, "Slim's sleeping out on deck somewhere. Wise guy. I think I'll do the same."

And at four o'clock he did, while White went to the bridge to take over the watch.

So nobody bothered about Roberts until a quarter to eight, when White went to look for him. He found his mattress on the boat deck, but no Roberts.

At eight o'clock, very annoyed but not at all worried, he told the chief officer, "I can't find Roberts, sir. I've found his mattress, but he must have crawled off somewhere else to sleep. I'll get Pickering to help me look."

"Wait till the steward bangs the breakfast gong," the chief officer advised. "That'll bring him fast enough."

It did not, and that was when people began to wonder. Roberts had never been known to miss a meal before.

By nine o'clock, after a full-scale search of the ship had failed to discover him, the chief officer reported to the captain.

"We've searched everywhere, sir," he said. "He's absolutely vanished."

"Rot!" snapped the captain. "People don't just vanish. You can't have looked properly. Search again. Get all hands on the job. Find out who saw him last, and when."

At half-past nine a fireman remembered seeing someone sitting on the rail aft smoking a cigarette. Nobody else had been doing that just then. Could it have been Roberts? Anyhow, no-body else had seen anything of him since he left the bridge at midnight.

At ten o'clock the captain, grumbling and vowing vengeance, turned the ship around.

"It's hopeless," he sighed, "but I suppose I've got to do it. Confound it, if he really went overboard he must be a hundred miles astern by now! What will the owners say about the delay?"

At the same time the wireless operator was sending messages out to Nassau, the United States Coast Guard, and any ships which might be in the vicinity—*Missing since midnight, one cadet, British, please report if sighted.*

Some hours earlier Roberts had opened his eyes. He closed them again quickly because of the glare, and growled, "Turn that light out, Pickles! Spoiling a chap's sleep . . ." But then he realized there was something peculiar about the glare and about everything else, and woke up.

The sun was already hot. His clothes were dry, and sand and salt had dried on his skin in ridges. Sand and salt were in his hair, eyes and mouth. He sat up and tried to get rid of some of it.

In one direction the white sand of the beach stretched far out of sight. In the other direction it gave way to a coral reef, and from the reef rose the skeleton steel light tower. Something seemed to be broken and dangling at the top of the tower, but for the moment Roberts was not concerned with that.

Inland the beach gave way to vegetation, and in among some palm trees was a low white house, about a hundred yards from the light tower and overlooking the reef. This was much more interesting to the cadet. Thinking of breakfast, he made his way toward it.

A couple of pigs ambled off, grunting at his approach. Some

hens were scratching around the house. But these were the only signs of life.

He banged on the closed door of the house. Nobody came. He shouted—"Hello, there! Anyone about?" Nobody answered except a cockerel, and he seemed to be trying to imitate Roberts.

Then he saw a smaller building beyond the house and went to it, but this contained only the diesel engine and dynamo for the light, and various stores. He found its door unlocked, but there was nobody inside.

He returned to the house, and this time tried the door. It was unlocked. He went in.

He found himself in a small living room, barely furnished with a wooden table, a couple of chairs, a cupboard or two, an oilstove, and a small radio transmitter and receiver. The last named showed signs of recent burning—some scorched metal and melted insulations. There was a faint smell of burned rubber about it.

Apart from that, the whole place was neat and orderly and very clean, except that on the floor near the table were a few cigarettes, as though someone had tipped them out of a pack.

Roberts picked up the cigarettes instinctively and put them on the table, and as he did so he saw that although they were a common English brand, they were shorter than usual.

That aroused his curiosity and he examined them more closely. He then saw that they had once been of normal length, but had been cut. The last two letters of the brand name were missing. More than an inch had been cleanly cut off each.

Puzzling about that, he passed on and found another room— a bedroom with two bunks built against the wall. One was tidily made; the other was stripped and bare.

Suddenly remembering that he was an intruder, he went outside again and made a fresh search for the lighthouse keeper. He wandered all around the place shouting, but only the pigs and poultry answered him. It was all rather eerie, he thought.

He looked up at the light tower again, wondering if it might provide a clue. There was only the dangling wire at the top, but that did not seem quite normal. When he came to examine it more carefully he decided it must be the radio's antenna. He found a broken wire on the ground, too, its insulation also burned.

"Struck by lightning!" he muttered. "I'm willing to bet that's what happened to it!"

Would that explain the absence of the lighthouse keeper? Had he gone off to another island, perhaps, to report the damage? Roberts looked for a boat but could not see one—only a little jetty built out from the reef, with a ringbolt and a loose rope attached.

"Hmm," he said to himself, "that seems to be that. I suppose I'll have to wait until he comes back."

And with that he began to think of breakfast once more. He returned to the house.

In a cupboard he found eggs, bacon, cereals, canned milk, —and canned everything else. In fact the big cupboard was full of food. It had evidently only recently been stocked, and for a considerable period.

"Well, I won't starve," he said with relief. "Now how does this stove work?"

That was fairly simple, too. The tank was full of kerosene; there were also matches and methylated spirits handy. Just in case of error there were full instructions printed on a card. There were pots and pans all ready for use, all beautifully polished. Evidently the lighthouse keeper was proud of his home.

"Probably an old sailor," Roberts thought. "This job would just suit some old sailor."

Half an hour later—at just about the time the gong was sounding on board the *Hopewell*—Roberts was sitting down to a breakfast which satisfied even him.

"Talk about uninhabited islands!" he sighed happily. "This one's absolute luxury!"

But luxurious eating means washing dishes. Roberts did not enjoy that so much, but he was too polite to leave it. The house deserved it. And there was plenty of water fed to the house from a tank on the roof, and a cupboard stocked with soaps and detergents of all kinds. There was no excuse for not keeping the place clean.

And in looking for cleaning materials he discovered another mystery. In one of the cupboards were several cans of cigarettes —the usual cans of fifty supplied for export, sealed with thin metal and provided with a cutter in the lid. But—*every can had been opened*. They were quite full, but opened. And the cigarettes in them were of the normal length, not cut like those he had found on the floor.

"Well, I don't know!" he exclaimed, shaking his head over this discovery. "I just don't know!"

And there was another odd thing, now he thought of it. The light had been burning until midnight. Who had started it going? Who had stopped it? When had the lighthouse keeper left the island? If he had gone suddenly in the night—why?

After he had put the room in order again Roberts went over to the engine house. There might be some explanation there— or more mysteries. Anyway, he was rather fond of engines.

It was a modern engine, and as well kept as the house. It had an electric starter, but when Roberts pulled the switch it only turned sluggishly and did not fire. There was also a large crack, but Roberts ignored it. He did not feel like hard labor in that heat.

On the other hand someone, somehow, ought to get the light going before nightfall. Supposing the keeper did not come back? Supposing a ship was wrecked because the light was not working? Even a temporary light of some sort, or a flare made from sacks soaked in kerosene, would be better than nothing.

"Oh, well," Roberts sighed, "I've never tried being a lighthouse keeper. I might as well have a shot at it."

He soon mastered the general features of the engine. Then he began a systematic examination of it. The first thing to check, obviously, was the fuel supply. And here he obtained immediate results. No oil was reaching the fuel injectors.

He traced back the fuel supply to a feeder tank. It was empty. He traced back further to a main supply tank. That was full. But between the two tanks was a valve, and that was closed. He opened it, and oil began to flow.

"It's too easy to be true!" he exclaimed, and he touched wood for luck before trying the starter switch again. Then he pushed it, and the engine started. He stood back and mopped his brow. It seemed impossible. And then he looked up at the lantern on the light tower, through the small window of the powerhouse, and he could see that the light was burning.

So it had gone out during the night simply because the engine had run out of fuel. Therefore the keeper must have started it going before he left the island. Well, it was something, though it left several mysteries unsolved.

He kept the engine running for several minutes while he experimented with valves and switches to make sure he could start it again if necessary, and while he was doing that he became aware of a shadow falling from the doorway behind him. He jumped around, and there was a man.

He did not look like the lighthouse keeper. He was wearing a smart cream tropical suit, a panama hat, white buckskin shoes, and he was smoking a cigar. He looked as though he had stepped straight ashore from his yacht—and that was in fact not far from the truth. In the background, moored at the little jetty, Roberts could see a small but very expensive-looking speedboat.

He stopped the engine hastily.

The man, smiling and showing a lot of teeth, waved the cigar in his hand and asked, "Where's Jake?" Roberts noted that he had an American accent. Then he had probably come from Florida, across the straits.

"Jake?" Roberts echoed. "Oh, if you mean the lighthouse keeper, he seems to have gone off in the boat somewhere."

The man's smile faded. He seemed puzzled. "Say, you're a queer guy!" he exclaimed. "Don't you know where he's gone?"

Roberts tried to explain. "No. You see, I only arrived during the night. He'd evidently gone before I got here. He must have left the light burning——"

The stranger interrupted him curtly. "Cut the rest. There's something phoney here. He knew I'd be coming today. You come on over to the house. I want the stuff whether Jake's here or not."

"The stuff?" Roberts asked—but the man was stalking toward the house. Roberts followed. When they both were in the living room the stranger closed the door.

"Now," he said, showing his teeth in a snarl instead of a smile. "Let's get down to business. Who are you, anyway?"

Roberts did not like him. He decided not to tell him more than was absolutely necessary.

"The name is Roberts," he said. "I told you, I came here during the night. When I woke up this morning——"

"Came here? How did you come here?"

"I swam," said Roberts with dignity.

The man almost leaped at him. "Swam! Say, are you trying to be funny? Cut it out, kid, or I'll drill you so full of holes you won't stop air!" And in his hand was a nasty automatic pistol.

"But it's true!" Roberts protested. "I fell overboard from a ship in the night—the *S.S. Hopewell,* if you must know—and swam ashore. I slept out on the beach. Here, look at this!" And he brushed sand from his hair.

The man lowered the pistol slowly. "Well, I'll be. . . . And you didn't see anything of Jake? You're sure he's gone?"

"I haven't seen a soul. The engine ran out of fuel soon after midnight and the light went out. He seems to have started it, and then gone off. Queer thing to do, but——"

"Queer!" the stranger cried. "I'll say it's queer!" And suddenly he picked up one of the cut cigarettes which Roberts had put on the table. His eyes narrowed. "Did these swim here?" he asked.

"I found them on the floor," Roberts said. "There are several cans in the cupboard behind you, but . . ."

The man did not wait for any more. He swung around, flung the cupboard open, and seized the cans. Finding them opened, he uttered a howl of rage. Then he tipped one up and shook its contents on the floor. He seized a second and repeated the performance, dancing and snarling meanwhile. He seized a third. . . .

But this was too much for Roberts. The room already looked like a circus fairground the morning after.

"You can't do that!" he shouted, and grabbed the man's arm. "Just look at the mess you've made! And it's not your house. . . ."

The man snarled afresh and turned to grapple with him. Roberts thoroughly lost his temper and went for him—and for the moment quite forgot the pistol which the stranger had put back in his pocket. Without that they were fairly evenly matched, for Roberts was heavy for his age and in fighting trim; the stranger was not a big man and evidently soft.

For a minute or two they surged to and fro, clawing at each other, grappling and wrenching, and trampling cigarettes into powder. Then they tripped over the coconut matting and fell, the stranger on his back and Roberts on top. There was a crash, a chair shot across the room as though catapulted, and the stranger lay still.

Roberts picked himself up. "I say," he said, "I didn't mean to be quite so rough, but you asked for it!"

The man did not answer. His eyes were closed and there was blood trickling in his hair.

"Oh, help!" Roberts muttered. "Supposing I've killed him?"

But the man was breathing regularly enough. The chair had merely knocked him out and punctured his skin.

It was then that Roberts remembered the automatic and quietly removed it. He put it in the food cupboard out of the way. Then he looked at the mess the room was in and groaned. All his hard work gone for nothing—and of course the hard work of the lighthouse keeper.

He had little doubt that the man was mad. Sane people did not come to uninhabited islands demanding "stuff" and tipping cigarettes all over the floor. Nor did ordinary law-abiding people carry automatic pistols and threaten to shoot shipwrecked sailors full of holes with them. And if the man had been mad before, what would he be like after that crack on the head?

Roberts decided to play for safety. He had had enough excitement for one day and night. He dragged the unconscious man into the bedroom, left him on the floor because he was too heavy to lift easily into one of the bunks, put a pillow under his head, and then proceeded to tie his hands behind his back with a length of light line—probably the lighthouse keeper's clothesline.

Then, for the second time that day, he set about cleaning up the living room. At least it gave him something to do.

Life had become rather complicated. He was no longer just a lonely castaway. He was not even merely a temporary lighthouse keeper. He was both of those, and in addition a jailer, and perhaps a male nurse as well. Supposing the man in the bedroom should die or go raving mad, or even remain unconscious for days and days?

Then Roberts thought of the speedboat down at the jetty. With that he could go and get help. But where should he go? There were other and bigger islands to the south, and probably some of them were inhabited. But which ones? Nassau, in the Bahamas, was a big town. But where exactly was Nassau? Or would it be easier to go across to Florida? And if so, should he take the cigarette man with him?

"Oh, what a mess," he groaned. "I'd rather be on board the old *Hopewell*. She was a bit of a frying pan, but I seem to have jumped clean out of the frying pan into the fire!"

He swept the smashed cigarettes up, put the whole ones back in their cans, tried to clean a bloodstain off the floor, failed and put the mat over it. Then he began to feel hungry again— and that made him wonder whether he ought to offer the stranger in the next room a meal if he woke up. Cooking for two meant washing dishes for two. Dash it, did he have to wait on the guy, along with everything else?

But a look at the man showed that he was still unconscious, or perhaps asleep. Roberts had a peaceful meal of corned beef, biscuits and canned fruit. That required no cooking and very little dishwashing.

The meal cleared away, he went down to look at the speedboat.

His eyes glistened at the sight of her. If only the *Hopewell* had a boat like that! All polished mahogany and chromium, automatic controls, a dashboard resplendent with dials—she'd be a joy to drive!

He pressed the starter, just to see if the engine would start. It did. And then the temptation was too much for him. He threw off the mooring rope, pushed the boat away from the jetty, and shifted gear. Just a short flip around—just to get the feel of her.

She went like a bird. He opened the throttle and she almost leaped out of the water. A great creaming bow wave threw spray back at the windshield. Roberts laughed for joy.

An airplane circled overhead, swooped low, and circled again. He waved to the pilot. Not even flying was better than this!

"Attaboy!" he yelled to a seagull, and opened the throttle as wide as it would go.

For a couple of minutes the boat fairly skimmed the water. Twenty-five knots? Thirty? Faster, at any rate, than Roberts had ever traveled afloat. And then—the engine stopped, just stopped dead without bothering even to slow down first.

Roberts' heart almost stopped with it, stopped and dropped like a stone. He knew what had happened, and it was no small matter like running out of gas. There was something he should have done to the cooling system or about the oil—something he had not done. The engine had overheated and seized solid. Probably it was completely wrecked.

At least another two minutes passed before he realized the situation completely. When he did his heart dropped even faster and farther than before.

He was adrift in someone else's expensive speedboat, which he had wrecked. He was almost out of sight of land, without oars or sail, without so much as a flag or a handkerchief, with the wide Atlantic on one side and the Florida Straits on the other. And he had left the owner of the speedboat shut in a bedroom on an uninhabited island with his hands tied behind his back.

He wondered in which country—Britain, the West Indies or the United States—he would be tried eventually, or in all three; and what the judge or judges would make of his various crimes, and where he would finally serve his sentence.

But after an hour or so of aimless drifting on the calm wind-less sea, he began to wonder if it mattered, because he would probably die of hunger, thirst, sunstroke or drowning. He imagined the boat being found months later, still drifting, with his bleached bones lying on the once-polished floorboards.

"I've got to do something!" he groaned. "Maybe the engine'll start now."

It would not, of course. And while he was struggling to start it manually since the electric starter refused to budge it at all,

He waved to the pilot. Not even flying could be better than this!

he was almost thrown into the sea by something crashing into the boat.

He grabbed at the engine casing, looked up, and gasped to see what appeared to be a small yacht alongside him. And while he gaped two men jumped down from the yacht into the speed-boat, seized him, pulled his hands behind his back and hand-cuffed him.

"Got you!" said one with satisfaction.

"Pity your boat broke down," chuckled the other.

"Look here . . . !" Roberts protested indignantly—but by that time he was being hoisted bodily on board the yacht. He noted in passing that she was flying a British flag—some sort of blue ensign. It was a little consolation but not much.

"I don't know who you think I am——" he began to protest, but again he was interrupted.

"Oh, we know who you are all right. We've had a description of you and your boat over the radio from Miami, Florida. You're Manuel C. Wyburn, otherwise known as Charlie Smith, otherwise known as Dodger Duke, and otherwise known by half a dozen other names according to the racket you happen to be working. Just now you're Manuel C. Wyburn, cigar manu-facturer with a business in Florida, only in reality you're smug-gling drugs. Right?"

"But—but I'm not a cigar manufacturer!" Roberts stam-mered. "And I don't smuggle drugs! My name's Roberts."

"And you just happen to be adrift in Wyburn's boat. Too bad, Charlie!"

"But—but I only borrowed it!" Roberts cried. "I—I thought I'd like to see how it went——"

"Well, well! And where did you borrow it from, Mr.—what was the name this time?"

"Roberts. It—it was from Turtle Cay. You see, I swam ashore there last night."

"You *swam* ashore there?"

"Uh—yes. And the man this boat belongs to came up to the house and tipped cigarettes all over the floor—I mean, I'd swept it once! So I went for him, and he hit his head on a chair, so I tied him up and went down to look at his boat, and—and I suppose I forgot to turn on the water or something!"

"The sun," said one of the men, shaking his head. "Poor beggar, he must have been out in it most of the afternoon—and no hat, either!"

"Better get him down below. Got a spare cabin, steward?"

"But—where are you taking me?"

A man in officer's uniform patted him on the shoulder kindly. "All right, take it easy. This is the lighthouse tender. We're just running in to Turtle Cay to put the keeper ashore. Not the one you knew. You didn't know Jake Turner had to go to the hospital with his appendix, did you? It's his relief we've got on board now. He opened the wrong tin of cigarettes, and that's how we've managed to catch you now. Bad luck, wasn't it? Anyway, we're putting him ashore, then we're going to look around the island for a poor drowned cadet off some British ship, and after that we'll take you back to Nassau. A nice big American policeman will be waiting for you there, to take you home to Florida."

"But—but dash it!" Roberts cried angrily, "I keep telling you —I'm not the man you think! And you needn't search the island for me, because I'm here. I mean, I *am* the drowned cadet you're looking for—only I'm not drowned!"

It took him half an hour to convince them, and even after that the two men who had handcuffed him, who seemed to be policemen, kept looking at him suspiciously and refused to allow him to go ashore when the ship reached Turtle Cay.

"Oh well," Roberts sighed, "don't blame me if the chap's got out and made a mess of the house again. You'll find his gun in the food cupboard, by the way."

So the policemen went ashore, and with them went the relief

lighthouse keeper and some men to repair the radio. When they returned to the ship Manuel C. Wyburn was with them, safely handcuffed.

He had not gotten out of the bedroom, but he was on the way. He had been trying to saw through the lashings on his wrists by rubbing them along the edge of a wooden cupboard door.

As the ship steamed away Roberts at last managed to solve all the mysteries.

It seemed that the previous lighthouse keeper, Jake Turner, had been taken ill just before the arrival of the tender with the month's supply of food, fuel and other necessities for the island. He had been taken off and another man left there temporarily.

Some hours after the tender had gone the temporary keeper had opened a can of cigarettes. He found to his astonishment that they were about an inch shorter than they should be—and shorter than the can they were in. Further investigation showed that the can must have a double bottom, and when the keeper looked closely he saw signs of fresh solder. He cut away the false inner bottom with his knife, and beneath it he found a number of tiny capsules containing a white powder.

He then opened all the other cans. A dozen out of a total of twenty cans contained the shortened cigarettes.

His next move was to try to communicate with Nassau by radio, but he found, as Roberts had suspected, that the set had been disabled by lightning. So he went off in his small motorboat to another island to telephone, taking the double-bottomed cans with him. But he knew he might not get back to Turtle Cay that same evening, and he started the lighting plant before he left. In his excitement he forgot, however, that the fuel cock behind the small feeder tank was shut. So the engine ran out of fuel at midnight.

All that night and next day the Nassau radio was busy. The United States police in Florida went into action. They discovered that Manuel C. Wyburn's speedboat had left the coast early, heading east. A plane was sent out to look for it.

"I saw one!" Roberts exclaimed. "I thought it was just messing about. Dash it, I waved to the pilot!"

One of the policemen nodded. "He reported it to us by radio. We were steaming straight for the lighthouse then, but we altered course to pick you up."

"But—what made you get in touch with the American police?"

The policeman shrugged. "It's obvious. Drugs aren't smuggled all the way from England to a lonely lighthouse near the American coast for nothing—not in those quantities. Remember this was only one consignment. Similar lots had been coming through every month. The United States was the obvious market for them. And as it happened the American police had already been watching Manuel C. Wyburn. Somebody recognized him as Dodger Duke from Chicago and guessed he wasn't in Florida just for his health. When they got our message yesterday they at once suspected him."

"But there must be dozens of people involved! I mean, who put the stuff in the cans?"

The policeman nodded. "A whole chain, right back to the cigarette factory, probably, and of course the people who stole the stuff in the first place. Jake Turner was one, but only one, and quite a small link in the chain. We've got him, and we've got Manuel C. We shall have to leave the rest to Scotland Yard."

"And what was the drug—do you know?"

"Heroin. Its manufacture is forbidden in the United States, but a certain amount is made in Europe for hospitals."

At seven o'clock that evening the wireless operator on board the *Hopewell* handed a message to the captain, who was having dinner in the saloon. The captain read it, and grunted.

"Roberts has been found," he growled to the chief officer.

"Alive and well and on board the lighthouse tender. She's steaming south to meet us. She can't be far away now. Apparently Roberts swam ashore to that island—Turtle Cay—the one with the light on it."

"Humph," said the chief officer, "I thought he'd turn up somewhere. Oh well, he's had a day's holiday. I'll make him work tomorrow to make up for it."

Port and Starboard

QUESTION: When is a board not a board?

Answer: When it is at sea.

Why? Because way back in Anglo-Saxon times the word *bord* sometimes meant a plank, and sometimes "side"; landsmen adopted one meaning, and sailors the other.

When you go *aboard* a ship you go over her side, not onto her planks. And when you go *overboard* you go over her side in the reverse direction!

Starboard means *steer-board*—the side on which the ship was steered when huge steering oars were used, before rudders were invented.

The opposite to starboard used to be *larboard,* and that meant the *lade-board,* or side on which the ship was loaded. For when she came alongside a pier the steering-oar side would be kept clear and the opposite side put to the pier.

The old terms remained after rudders were invented. *Starboard* and *larboard* were used for the two sides of a ship until about one hundred years ago. But when they were shouted in a gale of wind they were often confused through not being heard properly, and all sorts of accidents occurred. So someone invented the term *port* instead of *larboard,* and sailors gradually adopted it. Shipbuilders still use *larboard.*

Much more confusing was the way in which sailors clung to ancient steering orders.

After the steering oar came the tiller—a wooden bar attached to the rudderhead and usually pointing forward. To turn the ship to starboard—and to turn the rudder to starboard—the tiller had to be pushed over to port. So the orders were always given for the tiller, this being simpler for the helmsman. The order "port your helm" meant push the tiller to port, and so turn the ship to starboard.

Then steering wheels were invented, about 250 years ago. To produce the same effect—to turn the ship and rudder to starboard—the wheel also had to be turned to starboard (or clockwise). But the old orders were not changed. The captain said "Port!" And everything went to starboard—wheel, rudder, ship.

Not until 1930 was that arrangement altered—by law. And even then sailors protested and forecast all sorts of terrible accidents! However, it has worked well enough, and probably will do so until some new form of steering is invented.

Australian Gold

Ⓣ ED BURTON sat on an upturned box on the waterfront at Melbourne and stared at the dim lights of the ships lying at anchor in the harbor. There were twenty or more ships, tall sailing vessels of every type and nationality, all lying idle for want of crews to take them to sea.

This was the gold-rush year of 1854. The crews of the ships, and in some cases their officers, too, had deserted and gone to the gold fields. Half the inhabitants of Melbourne had gone— clerks and shopkeepers, laborers, and even the policemen.

Melbourne was a city of chaos. Its unpaved streets were choked with roistering miners back from the fields to spend the gold they had found. Its outskirts were vast camps of tents and shacks housing the thousands of immigrants who poured into Australia almost daily. There was no law or order. There was much drink and little food. There was fighting and shouting, weeping and misery, and dirt.

Ted Burton was sick of it all. He had come out to Australia a few months ago with his father, hoping to make a fortune and build a home to which his mother and the younger children could come. Now he was penniless and alone and wishing he had never come.

He and his father had reached the gold diggings. They had found a little gold after weeks of hard work and privation. Then Ted's father had contracted a fever which was sweeping through the camps and had died of it.

Ted had sold their few tools and other belongings, put their little store of gold into the pouches of his wide leather belt, and set out to walk back to Melbourne. He would take what he had back to his mother in England and advise her not to think about the new world any more.

There were many people on the road. Miners with gold in their pouches were swaggering back to town to spend it. Men fresh from England were marching forward hopefully with picks and shovels on their shoulders and sometimes women and children trailing behind.

Ted avoided the crowds as much as possible. He was afraid of being robbed. He knew there were gangs of men on the road who found it easier to take gold from others than to dig for it themselves. But he did not realize that such men, cowardly to the core, would look for the solitary traveler rather than those moving in crowds.

One evening as he was skirting the edge of a wood, looking for a comfortable place to sleep for the night under the trees, he stumbled right in among a dozen or so men sitting gambling around a campfire. Before he could dodge them they had leaped up and seized him.

"Oho!" cried one who seemed to be their leader—a great black-bearded man with a crooked nose. "A fly walks into the web, eh! Back from the diggings, mate? Why then, welcome to you—and take that belt from him, mates, for it's that heavy it's wearing him down!"

Ted had struggled, fought, kicked and bitten. But one boy

had no chance against a dozen men. Two of them held him easily while a third unbuckled his belt. He watched them tip his precious store of gold out in a little pile before the leader.

"Little enough," said the man scornfully, "but as it was no trouble to take we'll let him go. Here, take your belt, boy, and think yourself lucky we did not cut your throat."

"You brutes!" Ted gasped. "It was all I had! My father is dead and I was taking it back to England to my mother!"

The men laughed uproariously and drove him from the camp with kicks and blows.

"Tell your mother Black Shane sent you back to her!" the leader shouted, and then drew a pistol and fired it in Ted's direction.

There was nothing he could do. If he told other men on the road they would not interfere with such a powerful gang. His only hope would be in finding some of the soldiers who were trying to keep some sort of order on the gold fields, but the nearest might be fifty miles away.

So he staggered on and eventually reached Melbourne. There he thought himself fortunate to obtain work as a dishwasher in a cheap eating-house for the sake of his food.

Now, as he sat on the waterfront a week later, he was trying to decide what to do.

He might go back to the diggings and try to find more gold. Some people were lucky and found great nuggets just waiting to be picked up. Others worked for months and found none at all. And in any case before he could go back he would have to find enough money to buy more tools and a license to dig. That would mean getting a better job than he had at present.

The alternative was to persuade the captain of one of those ships out there to sign him on as cabin boy or deck hand and take him back to England. In that case he would have only his wages to take to his mother, and the news his father was dead.

He was still trying to decide what was best when the matter

was settled for him. Something hit him on the back of the head. He saw a sheet of flame and lost consciousness.

He awoke in what he knew to be a ship's fo'c'sle. It was a low narrow compartment, narrowing toward the bows of the ship. He was in a wooden bunk without mattress or blankets. The only light came from four small portholes; the hatch at the top of a vertical ladder was closed.

His head ached abominably. He hoisted himself up to look out of the porthole above him and get some fresh air from it, and saw that he was indeed aboard one of the ships at anchor in the harbor. Half a mile away was Melbourne and the water-front where he had been sitting the previous evening.

Then he saw that he was not alone in the fo'c'sle. Three or four of the other bunks were occupied, and in one a man was groaning.

"What happened to you?" Ted asked. "Were you knocked on the head, too?"

"Poisoned!" the man gasped. "That blasted crimp—oh, why did I trust him?"

"Crimp?" Ted inquired. "What's a crimp?"

The man sat up and stared at him. "Strike me, but you're a young innocent, ain't you? Crimp? Lodging house keeper, of course! Him as got me into his place and then put something into my beer and shipped me aboard this hooker! Here, boy, what hooker is it? Where's she bound?"

"I don't know," said Ted. "I've only just waked. I was hit on the head last night as I was sitting on the waterfront. But I'm not a sailor. They won't want me when they find out."

The man tried to laugh, but groaned instead. "They'll want you, all right. They'd make sailors out of sacks of shavings these days, they're that short o' crews. You wait till the mate sees you."

Ted had not long to wait, for almost immediately the hatch opened and a tall man dropped down the ladder.

"Now then, my beauties!" he cried. "Who's ready for work?"

"I don't mind work," said Ted, "so long as I can get some fresh air. My head is splitting."

The mate stared at him. "You're only a boy! Sink that crimp —we paid him for four men! How old are you, boy?"

"Fifteen, sir."

"Humph. Oh, well, I suppose we can make something of you, if it's only helping the cook. Up on deck, boy, and report to the cook. Now, what about the rest of you?"

Ted climbed the ladder, then paused to look about him. It was not many months since he had come out as steerage passenger in a ship very similar to this, so he was not quite lost. He could even look forward now to being a member of the crew. He had always felt very unimportant and very much in the way as a passenger in a crowded immigrant ship.

He saw the cook's galley—a little square box built on deck with a black chimney poking through its roof and smoke coming from it. But while he was making his way to it he heard noises coming from the fo'c'sle behind him and turned.

The mate and the groaning sailor were hoisting two other men up the ladder. Laying them out on deck, they proceeded to throw buckets of water over them. One man sat up, cursing. The other groaned and turned over, whereupon he received the contents of a second bucket.

Ted was glad he had awakened of his own accord.

He went to the galley and then found the cook—a shriveled little man with a wooden leg.

"The mate told me to report to you," Ted told him. "I'm to work for you, I think."

"Ho!" grunted the cook, looking him up and down. "Ho, you are, are you! And how did you come aboard, if I may ask?"

"I don't know," said Ted. "I was sitting on the waterfront over there last night when someone hit me on the head."

Without a word the cook spun him around, ran a hand gently

over his head, and suddenly clapped a wet cloth on it.

"Keep it on," he said. "It'll cool your brains, if you've got any. You can start by scouring them pans."

"What ship is this?" Ted asked. "Where is she bound?"

"Ship *Foreland* of London, and that's where she's bound when she's got a crew. How many came aboard with you?"

"I only saw three men in the fo'c'sle this morning. The mate has them on deck there now."

The cook looked out of the galley door and grunted. "One's a seaman and two ain't," he said. "I wouldn't be in the mate's shoes for anything this trip! Well, that's eight of us all told, counting the skipper, two mates, three hands, and you and me. Time they've found another eight or thereabouts I reckon we'll sail."

"Is the cargo on board, then?" asked Ted.

"All she's likely to get. A few tons o' wool and a few thousand pounds worth o' gold. That's her cargo this trip."

"Gold! Do you mean that?"

The cook snorted. "O' course I do! Boxes of it, down in the afterhold. There's gold being found, ain't there? 'Tain't no good in Australia, so it's got to be taken to England. That's logic. We bring miners out and take gold home. And gold is less trouble 'cause it don't want grub cooked for it. Go on, start working! Here comes the mate."

The mate put his head in the galley and nodded with satisfaction to see Ted working. "Keep him at it," he said. "Maybe we'll need him out on deck later, but if the men who are coming turn out to be seamen and not farmers like those two for'ard there, I may be able to leave him with you."

"How many are coming, then?" asked the cook. "You'd better let me know if you want grub for them."

"Ten. That'll do us, I reckon. The skipper sent word off from the shore this morning that he'd be bringing 'em out this afternoon. We're lucky. They're volunteers. Better have volunteers any day than the rubbish that the crimps scrape together."

"Scrape!" exclaimed Ted ruefully, feeling his head. "Some-one did more than scrape me!"

The mate laughed. "You'll do, boy. There are worse things could happen to you in Melbourne, I'll be bound. As soon as the skipper comes aboard I'll get you signed on articles. Do your work properly, and you won't regret being bumped on the head and shipped aboard the *Foreland*."

In fact Ted did not regret it now. He liked the mate, who seemed much less of a bully than some, and he liked the little cook, who he soon found out had been a seaman until he lost his leg in a shipwreck.

"Smashed between boat and ship when we was leaving her," he said calmly. "The surgeon chopped it off as soon as I got ashore. Bad, that was, but not the worst I've known at sea."

"Worse than shipwreck, do you mean?" Ted inquired. "Is anything worse than shipwreck?"

"Aye," said the cook darkly. "Fire is worse. Fire at sea is as bad as anything can be, and frightens men more than drowning. But it's because men get frightened that it's so bad. Nine times out of ten if they'd keep their heads it wouldn't be half so bad. Just remember that if ever the time comes."

"I'll try," Ted promised, but he hoped he would not have the experience.

In the late afternoon a large boat came off from the shore bringing the captain and the men he had found. Before it arrived the mate took the precaution of locking his other recruits down below. So Ted found himself shut in the fo'c'sle with the three men who had come aboard with him.

The one who had been groaning Ted thought was the best of them—a tough old sailor named Sam Croake who had de-serted from another ship, but was not really sorry to find him-self on board the *Foreland*.

"I've never been lucky," he said, puffing at his pipe. "I

shouldn't have found any gold if I'd got to the fields. Might as well be back aboard ship, and she don't seem a bad sort of hooker, considering."

The other two men had been farm laborers. They had been to the diggings, found a little gold, and come back to Melbourne to spend it. When it was gone the proprietor of the lodging house had given them free meals and bed, and had then drugged them and shipped them away. They still felt ill from the effects of the drug and their previous heavy drinking.

After an hour or so the hatch of the fo'c'sle was opened and the new men began to come down. The first to appear made Ted gasp with dismay. He was a burly, black-bearded ruffian with a hooked nose set crooked on his face—the man who had been the leader of the gang who had robbed him—the man who had called himself Black Shane.

He swaggered into the fo'c'sle, crying, "Well, shipmates, how goes it? All aboard the packet for London, eh!" Then he laughed, and the men following him joined in the laughter. Ted recognized several of them as members of his gang.

Ted shrank back into the shadows away from the square of the hatch, and when the men were all down he tried to slip past them and return to the deck. But the big man saw him and stopped him.

"What-ho, shipmate, don't you care for our company? Where away so fast?"

Ted's heart beat fast, but he could see that so far Black Shane had not recognized him. He kept his head down.

"To the galley," he said. "I'm the cook's mate. If you want any grub you'd better let me go."

The argument was successful. The men laughed and their leader let him go. But Black Shane warned him, "I'm the bosun aboard this ship now, so let's have a little respect from you, young shaver. And that goes for every one of you!"—he turned to the rest of the men and his beard jutted at them threateningly.

Ted ran to the galley. "Doctor!" he cried—the nickname for the cook of the sailing ship always being "Doctor"—"Doctor, the men who have just come on board are the gang who robbed me on the road down from the diggings! Ought I to tell the mate?"

The cook sharpened a knife thoughtfully. "Are you sure? It's easy to make a mistake."

"I'm absolutely sure! There's one with a black beard and a twisted nose—he's the leader. He calls himself Black Shane. He hasn't recognized me yet, but I expect he will when he sees me on deck. And Doctor—they volunteered! Don't forget that. Why should they volunteer? They aren't the sort of men to want to go back to England."

"Um-m," murmured the cook, testing the sharpness of the knife on his thumb. "No, that's right enough. I thought when I saw 'em come aboard they didn't look like homing pigeons. More like vultures, I thought—and Australia's the place for vultures, not England. Well, you'd better tell the mate. But don't blame me if it lands you in a packet of trouble."

Ted had his opportunity for telling the mate soon afterward, for he was ordered to go to the captain's cabin to sign the ship's articles.

He now saw the captain for the first time—an elderly man with a brown beard, kindly blue eyes and a deep rumbling voice.

"Name? You're being rated as cook's mate, wages three pounds a month. Are you willing to serve?"

"Yes, sir," said Ted. "I want to get back to England."

"Sign here, then. Can you write your name?"

Ted showed that he could. Some of the men had signed only with a rough cross. He could not see the name of *Shane* written anywhere. Then he plucked up his courage and spoke.

"Sir, on the way down to Melbourne from the gold diggings

I was robbed. Some men sprang on me and took all the gold my father and I had found. My father died on the fields, sir, and I was alone."

"Well, why do you tell me this?"

"Sir, the men who did it are aboard this ship now. The leader of the gang was the man with the black beard who says he is bosun. He told me his name was Black Shane."

The captain frowned. "Shane? He has signed articles as James Smith. Are you sure it is the same man, boy?"

"Quite sure, sir. I remember his nose, too."

The captain turned to the first mate. "He told me he was a seaman. What is your opinion?"

The mate nodded. "Deserter from a man-of-war, I should say. Tough as they make 'em, but I reckon I can handle him. The others aren't seamen, though three or four have some idea."

"Aye," said the captain, "that was what I thought." Then to Ted he said, "Boy, beggars can't be choosers, and we're in the position of having to beg for men these days. Those men have got to sail the ship home for us. When we reach England you can take your story to the police if you please, but I don't imagine you'll get much satisfaction. I'm sorry for you, but there's nothing I can do."

"It—it wasn't for me," said Ted. "It was for the ship. I mean, I couldn't understand why they had volunteered. They— they didn't seem that sort, sir—I mean, the sort who would want to go back to England."

"Humph. Well, that's our affair. I think we can look after the ship, eh, Mr. Dawkins?"

"Aye," said the mate shortly. "I reckon the second mate and I can deal with 'em."

Ted was sent away then. He had done all he could, but he was far from easy in his mind. The ship had gold in her cargo. Why had a gang of thieves volunteered to serve in her?

At all events the men were quiet enough that night, and next morning when the cry came, "All hands on deck!" they scrambled out of the fo'c'sle almost eagerly.

All was bustle and business then. "Hands to loose sail!" Those who were sailors showed the others the way. They swarmed out on the yards and loosed the gaskets which held the sails furled so that the canvas should be ready for setting. Then they manned the windlass and began tramping around it to hoist in the anchor cable.

"Stamp and go, boys! That's the way—and in she comes! England's around the corner and the girls are waiting for you!"

The men laughed and thrust against the great capstan bars cheerfully and the ship seemed to quiver with life.

Presently the anchors were swinging at the bows, waiting to be hoisted on deck and stowed. Topsails were set, and a jib to swing her head out from the line of anchored ships. Officers on some of those ships watched enviously as the *Foreland* set her nose for Port Philip Heads and the open sea.

In the afternoon the ship was clear of Port Philip—the great natural harbor of which Melbourne is the port. By sunset she was sailing eastward through Bass Strait, between Australia and Tasmania, and the land was only a dim cloud on the horizon. She had every sail set, and a westerly breeze was bearing her toward the Pacific—toward Cape Horn and the Atlantic Ocean beyond. Sailing ships homeward bound from Australia almost always took the eastward route by way of Cape Horn, for that way they were more likely to find favorable winds.

The men had been divided into two watches, port and starboard. The bosun and six of his cronies were in one watch, and this first evening were on deck from eight o'clock until midnight. The old sailor Sam Croake had been put in charge of the other watch with the five remaining men. They went to their bunks at eight and would be called at midnight to take over until four in the morning.

Ted, much to his relief, had been turned out of his bunk

in the fo'c'sle and been given a berth in the roundhouse—a house built on the deck near the galley where the petty officers normally slept. The bosun should properly have been sleeping there, but he said he preferred to be with his friends in the fo'c'sle.

That first night at sea Ted found it difficult to sleep, however. The noises of the ship kept him awake—the creak and groan of the gear and working of the timbers, the slapping of water against the side—and he was worried about the men who were his shipmates. He heard the bells struck for the hours—six bells at eleven o'clock, eight at midnight—and he heard the man on lookout reporting to the mate, "All's well!"

He heard the tramping to and fro as the port watch came out to relieve the starboard and the order, "Keep handy the watch!" which meant that one watch could go below while the other remained on deck.

After that all was quiet for half an hour, and then he heard a shout—a single shout cut short, followed by a thump as though something had fallen on deck.

Ted slipped from his bunk. He went to the open door of the roundhouse and looked toward the poop. The moon was low and did not give much light, but it was sufficient to enable him to see the figures of men moving about aft. There seemed to be more than the watch, and when he counted them he saw that there were at least eight—perhaps more. Then one stood up straight and for a moment was silhouetted against the sky, and Ted saw that it was Black Shane.

Something was wrong. That was clear enough. The bosun should have gone below with his watch at midnight. Yet Ted had heard no order for "All hands on deck." He looked for the second mate, who should have been on the poop, but could not see him.

Then most of the men disappeared, and it seemed to Ted they could only have gone below—down the companionway which led to the officers' cabins, where they certainly had no business at all. And a moment later he heard another single shout, quickly cut short as the first had been.

Ted ran back into the roundhouse and shook the cook.

"Doctor, wake up! Something's wrong! The men are all aft and I don't know what's happening!"

The cook grumbled and growled and refused to awaken, but at last he sat up and consented to listen. He even climbed from his bunk, strapped on his wooden leg, and stumped to the door.

Some of the men were coming for'ard then, and the cook hailed them. "What's on, then? Is it all hands on deck?"

A man laughed. "Nothing to worry you, Doctor. Sleep tight, my hearty—we don't want our breakfast yet."

They seemed to be clearing away gear from one of the boats, of which the ship had two, stowed on deck amidships.

"Aye, but what's happening?" the cook insisted. "Someone going ashore, then?"

The men laughed again, but did not answer. Instead the bosun's voice hailed from the poop.

"Stow the gab, there, and get that boat swung out! And when you've done it get those rats along out of the fo'c'sle!"

The cook stumped aft, followed by Ted, and one of the men shouted, "Here's the Doctor coming to see you about it, Boss— and the boy, too!"

Black Shane swore at them, and then growled, "All right, this is the way of it, if you want to know. We've taken the ship. I'm captain now. Anyone that doesn't like it can get out. That's what the boat's for."

"Not the cook, Boss!" one of the men shouted. "What about our breakfast?"

Black Shane laughed harshly. "Aye, that's right enough. And you'd better keep your mate with you, Doctor. Get back in the roundhouse, both of you!"

"It's mutiny!" the cook cried. "It's a hanging matter, and

I'll not be party to it. I'm calling you to witness o' that!"

The men laughed and thrust him back roughly into the round-house, with Ted on top of him. The door was slammed and fastened. Ted climbed to a bunk to watch through the porthole.

The boat was swung on a lift from the mainyard and pushed over her side. The ship was brought up into the wind to take the way off her. Then three muffled bundles were brought from aft, and Ted saw them to be the captain and two mates, securely gagged and bound. They were dumped roughly into the boat.

Three more men were now brought from for'ard—the three men who had come aboard with Ted. Old Sam Croake was struggling and swearing, but the other two were frightened and docile. They too were put into the boat.

"You'll get ashore somewhere," Black Shane told them roughly. "If you don't it'll be no loss. Take your choice of Australia or Tasmania, but if anyone wants to know say Black Shane has gone to South America. Eh, boys? Is it South America for us, with gold enough to last us all our lives?"

"Aye!" they cried. "Shove 'em off, Boss! Take us to America and be hanged to 'em!"

"South America!" Ted gasped. "That's where they're taking us, Doctor!"

The cook did not answer. He was sitting in his bunk with his head in his hands.

Ted watched the boat lowered and pushed off. Black Shane barked an order and the ship began to pay off before the wind again. Ted watched the boat drop astern for a minute, and then could see her no more. Then a man opened the door of the roundhouse and growled, "See we get a proper breakfast this morning! It's captain's grub from now on for all hands, and mind you remember it!"

"Aye," the cook muttered when the man had gone, "and more than captain's grub, if I'm any judge. Listen to 'em!"

The men had all gone aft. Lights showed in the captain's

and mates' cabins. There was shouting, and presently a clink-
ing of glass.

"They're at the spirits," the cook growled. "It's the first thing
mutineers always do, gold or no gold. It'll be a miracle if this
ship ever gets to South America or anywhere else. But it won't
last 'em long. Captain Wilkie never carried more than a few
bottles for the medicine chest, being teetotal himself."

One of the lights flared up suddenly, then went out. There
was more shouting.

"Knocked a lamp over," the cook muttered. "They'll have the
ship on fire, I shouldn't wonder."

And with that he gripped Ted's arm suddenly, and whispered,
"That's it! By golly, I've been wondering what we could do!
Now I've got it! Come on, lad, we've got to get busy while
they're drinking. It won't work once they're sober."

He drew Ted by the arm out of the roundhouse and to the
galley. "Those buckets of fat," he said. "Bring one."

Ted obeyed, wondering, and the cook led the way to the
fo'c'sle hatch. They went down with their buckets.

"Now," said the cook, "straw mattresses—slit 'em up, take
the straw out, and soak the sacking in the sea."

"But I don't understand!" Ted cried. "What are we going
to do?"

The cook chuckled. "Set the ship afire! Remember what I
told you about fire at sea frightening men more than anything
else? We're going to frighten these mutineers aft clean out of
their drunken senses!"

"But we can't burn the ship!" Ted protested. "That would
be as bad as mutiny!"

"We ain't going to burn her," chuckled the cook. "We're going to make 'em think she's burning. Smoke's what we want,
and a few flames, but mostly smoke. Wet those mattress covers,
and we'll start her going on those."

The cook had all the details worked out.

"Wet sacking, damp straw, the fat out of the buckets—there's some cotton waste in the 'tween decks, and some barrels of oil in the forepeak— Oh, we'll frighten 'em all right!"

They spread the material about the fo'c'sle, down in the forepeak under the fo'c'sle, in the cable locker, and along the 'tween decks. They broke out some bales of wool from the cargo and strewed that a foot deep under the main hatch.

At last the cook was satisfied and set a match to it. There was a flame for a little while, which they damped down with a wet sack. Then the smoke began to rise.

"Supposing it does set fire to the ship?" Ted asked, coughing.

"It won't—at least, not more than we can put out if we want to. You see, we know what's making the fire. They won't. That's what I'm banking on."

They staggered out on deck, rubbing their eyes. The smoke down below was already unbearable.

"Back to the roundhouse and into your bunk," the cook whispered. "Make out you're asleep. We've got to be as scared as the rest when it's discovered."

They lay down in their bunks. They could smell the smoke rising, but they had to wait a long while before anyone else noticed it, for the wind was astern and blowing the smoke away from the men aft.

The man at the wheel was the first to shout. Probably he had not had as much to drink as the others—and he was in the fresh air. They heard him jump, exclaim something to himself, and suddenly shout in a voice of panic, "Fire! Hey, Boss, quick! The ship's on fire!"

They heard some of the men grumbling. "Aw, hold your row! Give him another drink, someone! What's he shouting about, anyway?"

But Black Shane had rushed on deck, and now they heard his voice thundering, "Fire! All hands on deck! Sober up, you fools! Do you want to be roasted alive? Rig the pump, some of you! Get buckets—anything!"

Yes, he had been a seaman, but he was only one among many who had not. Rig the pump? How was that done? Where was the pump? Where were buckets? Where was the fire and how did it start?

Now that they were alive to the danger, panic gripped them. They rushed about aimlessly, falling over each other, blaming each other, even fighting with each other.

"Time we got out," the cook whispered. "It'll look fishy if we stay in our bunks. Rush about the way they're doing."

Ted staggered out, yelling "Fire!" at the top of his voice. The cook went stumping aft, shouting, "Why don't you clear the boat? She's all alight fore and aft!"

It certainly seemed so. Some men had rushed for'ard to the fo'c'sle, but staggered back, beaten by the smoke. Others had ripped the tarpaulin off the main hatch and flung the boards aside, and a great column of smoke was rising at them. Black Shane was struggling single-handed to get the pump working.

Now some of his men took up the cook's cry. "Lower the boat! We can't fight it! She'll go up like a rocket in a minute!"

"Stand away from that boat!" Shane shouted, and brandished a pistol at them.

Something came out of the smoke and hit him across the wrist so that he cried out with pain and dropped the pistol. Only Ted saw what it was—the cook's wooden leg.

The men ignored him and began hoisting the boat. Smoke from the hatch enveloped them, increasing their panic. They stumbled and gasped and swore, but somehow the boat was raised and swung.

Dawn was coming now. But the growing light only made the sight more frightening. Smoke was rising to the lower mastheads, blackening the sails. And suddenly even Ted gasped with fear

"Stand away from that boat!" Shane shouted, and brandished a pistol at them.

as a sheet of flame leaped out of the main hatchway with a mighty hissing and roaring.

That settled matters. The boat was swung over the side and men tumbled into her. Nobody bothered now to take the way off the ship. They fell in anyhow, and someone cut the rope. The boat sheered off from the ship's side. The last to board her was Black Shane, taking a flying leap into her and shouting to them to come back at the same time.

Ted watched the boat drop astern as only a few hours ago he had watched the other boat with the ship's officers in it. But this time the ship had not been stopped and was rushing on—wildly, with no one at the wheel.

Beside him the cook tried to laugh, but only succeeded in coughing. "They've not bothered about oars!" he coughed. "No sail, no oars— Lawks, what a crew! But come on, lad, we've got to put the fire out now. Never mind the ship. She'll sail herself for a while."

Under his expert direction they managed to get the pump working, and soon a stream of water was pouring down the main hatchway.

"Overdid it a bit there," the cook admitted. "I saw a spark and put a bucket of lamp oil down. It did the trick, but I was a bit scared myself the way the flame came up!"

"So was I!" Ted coughed, struggling at the pump. "I thought it was something we didn't know about."

After an hour's pumping the smoke died down in the main hatchway, and they moved the end of the hose to the fo'c'sle. The fire at that end did not take as long to put out because it had been burning longer and had not had the benefit of the cook's lamp oil.

At length they were able to look down at the filthy charred mess they had made, and the cook almost wept. "Cor, if the mate could see her now!" he groaned. "I reckon he'd shoot us!"

But the fire was out and the mutineers had gone. The ship and her cargo were safe—for the present.

The next problem was what to do with the ship. As the cook said, "She's a big lump to be sailed by half a man and a boy! And if we could sail her we wouldn't know where to take her. Navigation's double Dutch to me!"

They were alone now, with the ship sailing on toward the Pacific. The boat had long ago vanished beyond the horizon. There was not even a shadow of land in sight.

"At least we know Australia's somewhere to the northwest," Ted said. "We've got a compass. If we could get her turned around it would be something. The way we're going now we'll never get anywhere."

"That's right," the cook admitted. "First thing is to get some sail off her, and as we can't furl it properly we'll just have to let it fly. Now you do just what I tell you."

To take the weight of the wind out of the canvas they let go some of the sheets and halliards. The canvas bellied out and thrashed wildly, but the cook bade Ted ignore it.

"It can't be helped if it thrashes itself to pieces," he said. "We're doing our best, and that's enough."

Then Ted went to the wheel and turned it when the cook told him to bring the ship around to the port tack. And when they had her heading more or less to the wind they rigged tackles and very slowly heaved around the massive yards—normally hard work for six men. But at last they had the ship sailing very slowly in the right direction—approximately toward the coast of New South Wales.

She looked a wreck—filthy below and untidy aloft. And she was sailing anything but efficiently. But she was no longer heading for the Pacific.

It was an hour after that, when they were both eating their breakfast by the wheel, that Ted cried suddenly, "A sail! Look— to the westward!"

And then, as they watched the ship growing from a dim speck to a cloud of canvas, Ted cried again, "She's on fire, too! I can see smoke!"

He rushed for the main rigging and scrambled up it to get a better view, and then, within a minute or two, was shouting down and laughing excitedly. "She's a steamer! A man-of-war, I think! Yes—she's a steam frigate! Doctor, we're saved!"

But before he had returned to the deck he began to think they were anything but saved, for a gun boomed from the frigate and a shot entered the water just ahead of the *Foreland*.

"That's heave-to!" the cook cried scornfully. "Cor, what does he think we're doing?"

Nevertheless he spun the wheel to bring the ship right into the wind and instructed Ted to let go all the remaining sheets. The ship lay rolling with all her canvas and gear flapping and slapping against her spars.

Soon the man-of-war also hove-to, and the contrast was a lesson in seamanship. Her sails disappeared as though by magic. She lay stopped, and almost before she had stopped a smart cutter was dashing away from her side. In it were a party of bluejackets armed to the teeth, with the blades of their cutlasses bared to the sun, and a dozen redcoated marines in addition.

Amazement and explanations followed. The naval party had expected to find a ship full of desperate mutineers, for they had already picked up the captain and officers of the *Foreland*.

"A one-legged cook and a boy!" their lieutenant cried. "Well, if that don't beat cockfighting!"

So far as Ted was concerned it had also beaten him. Suddenly he was dog-tired. Blackened and filthy as he was, he only wanted to crawl into bed.

It could not be, however; he had to go on board the frigate, meet her officers and the officers from the *Foreland*, go through the whole explanation again and yet again and answer a thousand questions.

He supposed it was worth it, for he had not shaken hands with a real naval officer before, and now he did it with a dozen in quick succession. So did the cook, wiping his hand on the seat of his trousers after each one before going on to the next.

And it was certainly worth it when, back on board the *Foreland* and being towed by the steamer toward Melbourne, Captain Wilkie told him and the cook, "You two have saved the insurers a loss of nearly a hundred thousand pounds. You can't claim salvage, because you're members of the ship's crew. But you'll get a reward. How would one per cent of the value suit you?"

"One per cent—why, that's a thousand pounds!" Ted gasped, doing rapid arithmetic in his head. And then he thought of his mother in England and of what a thousand pounds would mean to her.

"I don't believe it, sir," said the cook firmly but politely. "I just don't believe there's as much money as that in the world!"

Distances, Nautical Style

SAILORS measure distances differently from landsmen—and more sensibly.

A *land* or *statute* mile equals 5,280 feet by government decree. But a *nautical* or *sea* mile equals 6,080 feet because that is the length of a minute of longitude measured along the Equator. Thus the circumference of the earth measured along the Equator is 360 degrees, which equals 21,600 minutes (multiply by 60) which equals 21,600 nautical miles. Convert that in terms of feet, and it comes out to 24,873.27 land miles. Much more awkward!

A *cable* equals a tenth of a sea mile, and gets its name and its length from the old hempen anchor cables which were usually made to that length, or about 100 fathoms.

A *fathom* is six feet, and is taken from an old word meaning the span of a man's outstretched arms, which does measure about six feet. Sailors still measure rope approximately with their arms outstretched, fathom by fathom. But apart from measuring rope the fathom is used mainly as a measure of depth of the sea. Nobody talks about the length of a ship, for instance, as being so many fathoms.

A *knot* is a measure of speed, not distance, and means one sea mile per hour. It comes from the old sailing ship method of measuring a ship's speed by running a log line out astern, with a piece of wood (the log ship) standing upright in the water to "anchor" it—rather like a kite on the end of its string. Knots were tied in the line at certain equal distances, and the passing of the knots was then timed by an officer holding an hourglass. The distance between the knots and the time taken for the sand to run through the glass would be worked out in relation to each other, and the result would quickly give the ship's speed in nautical miles per hour—or knots.

The Brave Innocents

It was Saturday afternoon. The cadets of the British cargo steamer *Hopewell* were toiling at the oars of the ship's heavy dinghy, rowing steadily eastward away from the land, in search of a breeze which would enable them to set their sails and really enjoy what the chief officer had been pleased to call "a little boat practice."

Astern lay the coast of Mexico—low, monotonous, with surf-ridden beaches backed by gray-green cactus scrub. The *Hopewell* itself was at anchor a mile outside the little port of Tomaso, too shallow for it to enter, awaiting the cargo which would be brought out to it by lighters on Monday morning.

Said White, the senior cadet, as he glanced over his shoulder, "There's a steamer coming in. For Pete's sake, brisk up as we pass her, or she'll think we're in distress!"

Puffed Roberts, his immediate junior, "Brisk up! Give me strength! I'm a grease spot already!"

Young Pickering, who was in his first year at sea, also glanced over his shoulder at the incoming ship, and sighed. "Her smoke's going straight up. Not a blessed breath of wind anywhere! Look, Jumbo, can't we chuck it? I'm just about beat!"

Perhaps White had only been waiting for someone else to suggest it. At all events, he too sighed and relaxed. "Okay. Easy all. Rest on your oars."

They eased their aching muscles and mopped their brows, and turned to look at the approaching ship.

"It's only a baby!" Roberts scoffed. "It's one of those coasting schooners. I thought you said it was a ship!"

"Did you ever see a motor schooner making smoke?" White demanded. "She's making more than the old *Hopewell* does when we're cleaning fires!"

Young Pickering, who scarcely liked to disagree with his seniors, nevertheless asked in a puzzled voice, "Why is the smoke coming from her bows, Jumbo? I never saw a steamer with the funnel in the bows!"

They all stared. Pickering was right. If this was a steamer it was certainly a queer one!

Suddenly White exclaimed, "It *is* a motor schooner! That's her exhaust funnel right aft, but that's not where the smoke is! It's my bet she's on fire! By golly, she is! Look at that smoke pouring out now! Come on, pull! Pull till you bust!"

They grabbed their oars again. They forgot the heat and their sore muscles. They pulled as they themselves would not have believed possible a few minutes ago. The heavy boat almost surged through the water.

The schooner seemed to have stopped. Smoke lay like a pall on the water. Soon they could smell it, and their eyes began to water.

"We'll go around it and get under her stern," said White. "Pull, Slim! Get some of that fat down. Pickles, stand by for'ard and grab her rail when you can. Hitch the painter somehow."

Pickering shipped his oar and scrambled forward. The boat swung around and he crouched, waiting.

"Easy! Way enough! Now!"

He grabbed the rail, flung the rope over it and hitched it.

"All fast!"

He swung himself up to the rail and over it like a monkey. Roberts followed more sedately because of his bulk. White kicked the dinghy clear of the ship's side before following them. They all ran forward.

It was an old sailing schooner about seventy feet long, with her masts cut down and an engine installed aft. The engine was stopped. Amidships was a large cargo hatch, battened down. Forward was a small scuttle hatch, evidently the entrance to the crew's quarters, and from this great volumes of smoke were pouring.

"But where are the crew?" gasped Pickering, who had led the rush.

"Dead, if they're down there!" replied White grimly.

"Not on your life!" cried Roberts, pointing out over the side. "There they go, the rats! Abandoned ship, by hookey!"

The boat was less than half a mile from the ship. Its oars flashed in the sunlight. The motley colors of its crew's shirts could still be seen.

"They must have been just leaving as we arrived!" White exclaimed. "The smoke hid them from us. Well, I'm . . ." He looked around the decks and muttered, "Now, I wonder . . . Maybe the pump jammed!"

By the mainmast was an old-fashioned pump with cross levers and handles for two men. Attached to it was a decrepit canvas hose, still dripping water.

White ran to it and pumped vigorously. Water gushed from the hose.

"It beats me!" he cried. "A perfectly good pump, an ocean

full of water, yet . . . look here, what about showing 'em up?
We could try, anyhow."

"Salvage!" Roberts gasped. "By golly, if we save the ship
we can claim salvage money. What's her value, Jumbo? And
there's the cargo, too. . . ."

"Mercenary beggar!" White jeered. "Right. Pickles—you
and Slim take the pump. I'll see what I can do with the hose.
We ought to be able to flood that fo'c'sle. It's not very big."

He soaked his handkerchief and tied it around his mouth
and nose, then plunged into the smoke. For awhile only the
movements of the hose indicated his presence.

They could hear the fire raging down below. There was a
fierce hissing as water reached burning wood or hot metal on
deck. Steam mingled with the smoke.

Then White staggered back to them, blackened and gasping
for breath.

"It's the galley!" he gasped. "Stove must have blown up. I
can't get below, but the galley chimney's red hot and the deck's
smoldering around it. I want to smash the chimney. Where's
a battering ram?"

Roberts pointed to an iron bar used for securing the tarpaulin
over the main hatch. White nodded, took it, and plunged back
into the smoke.

They heard him battering at the chimney, and presently there
was a crash. Flame spurted upward, but died again.

He staggered back to them again and collapsed on deck, panting. When Pickering would have gone to his help he was
waved back. "Keep pumping! I'm all right!"

When he could speak more or less normally he told them,
"I've jammed the hose down the chimney hole. It's getting right
to the heart of things. If we could get the hatch closed to shut
off the air . . ."

"It's my turn," said Roberts. "Take the pump, Jumbo."

*Blinded and holding their breath they tugged at the sliding hatch
cover, but it refused to move.*

"It'll need two," said White, and Pickering sprang after Roberts.

They made masks of their handkerchiefs as he had done, and dived into the smoke together. Blinded and holding their breath, they tugged at the sliding hatch cover, but it refused to move. Then, almost together, they found securing hooks and released them. The hatch slid forward. The main source of smoke was cut off. At once breathing became easier.

"Nice work!" White greeted them. "I expect the portholes are open, but that'll stop the through draft. Slim, your own mother wouldn't know you!"

They were indeed all as black as coal trimmers. Their once-white shirts and shorts were unrecognizable. White was soaked from working with the hose.

But appearances did not matter. They pumped steadily, and water poured through the hose.

"What happens when we've emptied the Gulf of Mexico?" Pickering inquired. "Do we start on the Atlantic?"

Then Roberts, panting, asked plaintively, "How much water *does* that fo'c'sle hold? It ought to be full to the deck by now."

White pulled the hose from the chimney hole and lowered the iron bar into it. "It is—nearly," he shouted, and abruptly sprang to the ship's side.

"Avast pumping," he cried. "You're sinking her."

They dropped the pump handles and ran to the side, and gasped. The ship's bows were low in the water. The sea was lapping gently into an open porthole. From the same porthole, and others, smoke was rising slowly, no longer in billowing clouds but in wisps.

"We can't let her sink!" Roberts groaned. "What about our salvage money?"

"She won't sink," said White curtly. "The stern is high enough. The main thing is to make sure the fire's out."

He slid back the scuttle hatch. Smoke rose from it lazily and cleared gradually. After a minute or two White climbed into the hatch and went down a couple of steps.

"I'm in water now," he reported. "I can't even see the galley. The stove must be under water. Gosh, it's up to the top bunks in the fo'c'sle. And what a mess! They must have been boiling oil, I think."

He came out again. His canvas shoes were thick with sooty grease.

"Well, what next?" he asked. "Do we just sit here and wait till help comes?" Then he frowned, and wondered, "Why hasn't anything come out from the shore already? The crew must have landed ages ago. You'd think somebody else would get the idea of salvage besides us."

"Let 'em try!" Roberts cried truculently. "We aren't letting anyone else butt in. She's ours. We've done the work."

"So far," White agreed. "But somehow we've got to get her ashore. We'll need a tug. . . ."

But at that point Pickering, who had strolled aft, returned and asked casually, "Why not start the engine?"

They jeered at him. "Where's the engineer? Do you know anything about diesels?"

"Yes," he said calmly, "I do. I've just been looking at this one, and it's practically the same as the one in my uncle's tractor, only a bit bigger. I've been messing around with that tractor since I was ten."

They gaped at him. Then White slapped him on the back and Pickering staggered.

"Pickles, you genius. Come on. We'll probably have to go stern first. If we try going ahead we'll push the fo'c'sle under."

They raced aft. Pickering led the way into the tiny engine room. White followed easily enough, but Roberts panted and yelled when the others hurried him.

"It's a heavy job," Pickering warned them. "It'll take some swinging."

"We'll do the swinging while you twiddle the knobs," said White. "Say when."

Pickering stationed himself at the controls. "Ready? Now!"

They swung heartily. Nothing happened.

"Again!"

They swung again. Roberts banged his elbow.

"Again!"

The engine coughed, muttered, and stopped.

"Nearly! This time!"

And this time it was. The engine coughed, muttered, and kept on muttering. Pickering opened the throttle gently. The engine responded noisily.

White extricated himself and scrambled back on deck.

"Wrong way!" he shouted. "We're going ahead!"

Pickering rammed the gear lever over. The steel clutch grated and shrieked. The propeller churned madly under the stern.

"Okay! Keep her at that." White ran to the steering wheel. The ship gathered sternway and began to turn. Then something bumped against the side.

"The dinghy! Oh, no! I'd forgotten. . . ."

Roberts popped from the engine room hatch like a cork from a bottle and dashed to the side. He unhitched the painter, towed the boat forward, and hitched it again.

"No damage done, thank goodness," he reported. "I should hate to pay for a new dinghy out of my salvage money. I want to buy a motor bike for my next leave. How much do you think we'll get, Jumbo?"

"We haven't got the ship in port yet," said White tersely.

Progress was obviously going to be slow. The ship could only make two or three knots astern. Her tubby counter pushed the water aside instead of cutting through it. The submerged fo'c'sle dragged behind her like a broken cart behind a laboring horse.

Slowly they approached the *Hopewell*.

"Take her close, Jumbo," Roberts urged. "Let 'em have a look at us!"

But White shook his head. "She's steering like a barrel. I'm not taking any chances. We'll be lucky to get her inside the river safely."

However, they did pass close enough to see the puzzled faces of the *Hopewell's* crew lining her rails, and Pickering celebrated the occasion by producing a piercing blast from the schooner's exhaust siren.

"Sounds like a brass hen laying a tin egg," Roberts said.

A few minutes later White warned them, "There's a launch coming out. Now remember, we don't want any help, except maybe a pilot to take us into the river. We're doing fine."

The launch drew near. They could see several passengers in it—men in white or cream suits and Panama hats.

Roberts exclaimed, "One of them's Sancho! You know, Jumbo—the pilot who took us to the anchorage."

White sighed with relief. "At least he can speak English. I was trying to remember my Spanish."

Rather to their surprise the launch did not come alongside at once. It turned and chugged along beside them a good hundred yards away.

White shouted, "Sancho! We want a pilot! Are you coming aboard?"

The heads of the passengers wagged together. After quite a while Sancho shouted, "Who are you?"

"Cadets off the *Hopewell,*" White retorted. "Come on, man. What's the matter?"

There was another excited conference in the launch. Then came the question, "How is the fire?"

White snorted disgustedly. "Is that what they're scared of? That crew must have pitched a good yarn!" He shouted across the water, "Fire's out long ago. The fo'c'sle's flooded. If you don't hurry we'll probably get stuck on the bar."

Then at last the launch turned toward them and came alongside.

Sancho, small, wiry and fussy, sprang aboard lightly, saying almost before he was on deck, "Steer more to starboard, please. You see the buoy? Steer for the buoy."

Next came a tall man in immaculate white uniform. It was not quite as white or immaculate by the time it had collected some of the soot from the schooner's rail.

"Señor José de Santos y Alvarez, Captain of the Port," Sancho introduced him. The captain bowed low.

The third arrival, and the last, was a stout man in a cream Palm Beach suit, whom Sancho introduced as "Señor Miguel Horros, the owner of this vessel." Señor Horros also bowed low.

The two Mexicans gazed suspiciously at the occasional wisps of smoke which were still rising from the fo'c'sle. They stared rather more than suspiciously at the begrimed cadets.

"Look here, Sancho," White whispered hurriedly, "we've put out the fire and we mean to claim salvage. Your friends had better understand that."

"Ah, *si!*" exclaimed the pilot, waving his hands and explaining rapidly in Spanish.

"Ah, *si!*" echoed the captain of the port.

Señor Horros sighed and shrugged his shoulders and muttered something in Spanish.

"It is understood," said Sancho. "The ship has insurance. The insurance will pay salvage."

"That's fine!" Roberts cried, beaming. "I mean, we don't want to be tough, but we do think we deserve it. We had quite a job putting the fire out, you know."

Sancho turned his attention to the steering. "Starboard more, please! Just to pass the buoy, you understand?"

Suddenly the captain of the port astonished them by standing at attention and saying in halting English, "You—is—'eroes!"

"Heroes!" Roberts protested. "Oh, I say. . . ."

Pickering grinned and blushed.

"Because—of ze cargo—no?" said the captain of the port, and he spread his hands, puffed out his checks, and added, *"Boom!"*

The cadets gaped at him.

Señor Horros beamed delightedly because evidently he could understand this, and added, *"Boom! Grande explosivo—si!"*

The cadets appealed to the pilot. "Sancho! What on earth does he mean?"

Sancho, satisfied that the schooner would not actually hit the buoy, found time to explain.

"It is the cargo—down here in the hold. It is for the mines up the river—for the blasting, you understand? For the blasting of rocks. It is many tons—er—dynamite, and gun—ah, *si*—guncotton—is it not? It is not happy to have a fire on board with such cargo, I think?"

"Oh, gosh!" they gasped. "Oh, golly!"

The captain of the port spread his arms wide. Without warning, and ignoring the soot, he suddenly embraced Roberts, who happened to be nearest, and planted a kiss on his smutty cheek.

"Mi inocente bravo!" he cried. "My brave innocent!"

And at that moment poor Roberts would willingly have sacrificed all his salvage money to be able to hide his embarrassment.

Landsman, Beware!

"YOU'VE never seen the Equator? You don't believe it can be seen? Why then, just take a squint through this telescope!"

Oh yes, the innocent passenger sees the Equator all right—a faint line stretching across the sea. In reality it's just a strand of thread skillfully held across the lens of the telescope by the ship's captain!

That is only one of the tricks sailors play on landsmen; they play many more on the ignorant apprentice on his first trip out.

If you go to sea you will of course hear of many strange things which do in fact exist: fids[1] and fiddles[2] and donkeys' breakfasts,[3] gripes[4] and bitts[5] and samson posts.[6] But beware of being sent for a "bucket of vacuum." Just laugh when you are warned not to put the paint on inside out. And if anyone tells you to fill the green starboard sidelight with green oil, or the red port light with red oil, just remind him that a ship's lights are all electric these days!

[1] *Fid:* pin used for splicing rope; a marlinspike.
[2] *Fiddle:* rack for dishes in rough weather.
[3] *Donkeys' breakfasts:* straw mattresses.
[4] *Gripes:* the forward ends of dished keels of steel ships.
[5] *Bitts:* heavy posts fastened to decks, around which mooring lines are wound.
[6] *Samson posts:* posts supporting deck beams.

One young apprentice was sent by the chief officer to the boatswain for the key of the keelson[1] locker. The boatswain said he didn't have it and sent him to the carpenter. The carpenter sent him to the engineer on watch in the stokehole, and that officer sent him to another on watch in the engine room. Here the quest was ended, and the sweating apprentice was presented with a huge spanner[2] weighing over a hundred pounds.

He staggered with it to the deck, where a sympathetic seaman told him it was all just leg-pulling, a practical joke. The keelson "locker" does not exist and it has no key! This particular apprentice was willing to go through with the joke, however. He carried the mighty spanner to the chief officer's cabin, where that important gentleman was by now enjoying an afternoon siesta. Onto the sleeping form the apprentice dumped his weighty "joke." "Key of the keelson locker, sir!" he cried brightly, and left hastily before the storm broke!

[1] *Keelson:* a supporting structure of the ship; usually a horizontal I beam on a steel ship.
[2] *Spanner:* wrench.

The Pilot

It was the year 920. Two Saxon boys, sons of the Thane of Bradston in Essex, were fishing from their boat off the River Colne. Edgar, the elder, was fourteen years of age. Alstan, the younger, was twelve.

Edgar was baiting his hooks in the bottom of the boat when Alstan gripped his arm and said in a tense whisper, "Edgar, look seaward! A ship!"

She was standing in from the east, far out on the horizon as yet, and little more than a square speck of sail. But presently as the boys stared they saw the sun sparkling on flung spray, and they knew it to be the result of oar blades—many oar blades—rising and falling rhythmically as they drove the ship onward. For the wind was light and the sail would scarcely give the ship steerage way.

Then again the sunlight flashed on something—not spray this time but something made of shining metal—and Edgar muttered, "A shield—or a helmet."

"Or the dragon's head at her prow," Alstan whispered. "Father has told us how they sometimes gild the dragon's head with thin metal."

"Aye, and even gold if the ship belongs to one of their great chieftains," Edgar agreed, not taking his eyes from the approaching ship.

Neither of the boys had actually seen a Norse pirate ship before. Their father had seen them often enough as a young man—great fleets of them—and he had fought with King Alfred against them. But Alfred had forced the Danes to make peace, and his son King Edward had driven them into the far north of England. The only Norsemen who remained in the south were peaceable men who had turned farmers and who now hated the occasional Danish pirates as much as the Saxons.

And those who did come in these years of peace were the worst sort. They were as lawless in their own countries as when they landed in England to burn and murder and steal.

So the Thane of Bradston and every farmer and inhabitant of the English coastal villages kept constant watch for them, knowing that if they were not vigilant they might at any moment lose their homes, their cattle, and even their lives.

Edgar, who had been thinking of all this while he watched the oncoming ship, suddenly made up his mind.

"She's a pirate, Alstan. I'm sure of it now. They have seen the smoke from our fires at home and are coming in to investigate. Take your oar, quickly. We must warn Father!"

They rowed frantically then, and the little boat surged to the pull of the oars. But only a few miles behind them forty great sweeps, pulled by powerful men and aided by the bellying sail, were driving the pirate ship after them. Unless the villagers had already seen it they would have little time in which to drive the cattle into the marshes for safety and carry their few belongings out of their houses. The houses themselves would almost certainly be burned, but they were only mud and thatch and could be rebuilt. Cattle and furniture could not so easily be replaced.

But Edgar had formed a plan and he talked now as he rowed.

"We are heading straight for the shore over the mud banks. The ship cannot follow us this way and will head for the mouth of the river. As soon as we touch you must jump out and run to tell Father. You know the short cut through the marshes."

"But you, Edgar—will you be with me?"

"No. I'm going to take the boat out to meet them. I must delay them if I can. I think they are still too far away to see you land. I'll row right into their path and they will stop to ask me about the village. Perhaps I can persuade them to leave us alone, for we are poor people and have little to steal. If I cannot, at least I can delay them and give our people more time to get the cattle away."

"But they may kill you!"

Edgar shook his head. "They will not bother with me. But they would kill Father and the other men if they stayed to fight. There are forty of them at least, and in all the village we could not find six men fit to bear a sword!"

"But there are more at Colchester, Edgar! If we could get them——"

"Father will attend to that. Perhaps he will send someone on horseback. But even if he does it will take hours. Tell him I will do my best. . . ."

The boat grounded softly, and Edgar seized the second oar from his younger brother.

"Run—as quickly as you can! Don't bother about me!"

Alstan breathed, "Good luck, then!" and sprang over the side. Edgar backed the boat away from the shore into deep water as he watched his brother wade ashore, pause a moment to make sure of his route through the salt marsh and sedge grass, and then begin to run.

Edgar rowed the boat easily, heading across the river mouth

in order to lay her well in the path of the pirate. But he did not want to give the impression of being in any hurry or state of alarm.

In fact he had scarcely recovered his breath from the frantic pull ashore before a shout from the Vikings showed that they had seen him, and the oarsmen rested on their oars to let the ship come up to him.

Wishing his heart would not beat so furiously, he hailed the ship. "Who are you? Where do you come from?"

The steersman, a great bearded fellow wearing bronze helmet and breastplate, but his clothes made mainly from skins like those of the rest of the crew, answered with a shout mingled with laughter.

"Oho, the young cock crows! Hoist him aboard, Olaf, and let us hear him crow to more purpose!"

The ship was almost stopped now. Edgar pulled suddenly and desperately at his oars, trying to get his boat away from her. But a man reached out after him with a long hooked pole, grappled his boat and drew her close. Another man reached downward with huge arms outstretched, and abruptly he was lifted through the air, swung high above the rowers' heads and down between their benches. His captor thrust him roughly aft while the men greeted him with raucous laughter.

They were all great muscular men, hairy and bronzed by exposure to sun, sea and air. They seemed good-humored enough at present, but he knew they would kill him without compunction if the mood took them, and laugh as merrily at the joke of it. Their own lives were constantly in danger, and they cared nothing for the lives of others.

Their talk sounded rough to him, but he understood it well enough. Saxon and Danish, Frisian, Swedish—they were but dialects of the same language.

"Push his boat clear of the oars, Olaf," the steersman commanded. "He will not need that again."

Edgar gritted his teeth as he saw the man Olaf not only thrust the boat away with his pole, but smash its bottom in and leave it waterlogged and sinking.

"Why did you do that?" he demanded. "What do you want with me? I have done you no harm!"

The steersman laughed coarsely and grabbed his shoulder. Edgar winced at the pain of the strong fingers biting into his flesh.

"Ho, my young Saxon cock, but you have too much to say for yourself. Do you know who I am?"

"No," Edgar retorted. "I asked you before you pulled me aboard, but you would not tell me."

"Ha! Then learn now, young cock-sparrow. I am Thorvald, surnamed Sharp-Tooth, and this is my ship *Dragon's Spear*. Have you heard of me?"

"No, I have not," Edgar replied, and wondered whether Alstan had reached the village yet.

"Then you shall!" cried the steersman harshly. "You and all your Saxon brood! What is the name of yon village, boy?"

"It is called Bradston."

"How many people are in it?"

"Not more than twenty, with women and children and villeins."[1]

"There will be twenty less when Thorvald Sharp-Tooth has finished with it! But it is food and drink we need. You have cattle and sheep in your village, boy?"

"A few, sir, but poor beasts and scarcely worth the taking, for the grazing has been poor this year."

"Don't lie to me! All you Saxons are liars, and all your beasts are fat, as you are yourselves. Fat and lazy, you Saxons are, and no fit meat for our swords. But we may have sport chasing you among the marshes, for we grow stiff with sitting at the benches and need exercise. How say you, lads?"

---

[1] Peasants, or tenant farmers.

"Aye!" they cried in a great roar. "Take us into the river, Thorvald, and let us get at the Saxon clods!"

Thorvald Sharp-Tooth laughed. "You hear, boy? The dogs are howling to be unleashed. Now answer me, and answer truthfully—is this river of yours as wide and deep as it looks?"

"No, sir. There are many mud banks and only a narrow channel deep enough for a ship as big as this."

"Well, that is truthful, for I know it myself. All the rivers and inlets on this coast of England are the same. If you had replied that it was wide and deep I should have known you for a liar and my sword would have taken the head from your shoulders. But you know the channel, boy?"

"Yes, sir. All the people here know it."

"Then you shall show it to us—and listen, boy, for I have taken a liking to you. You have more spirit than most Saxons and might well make a Viking. If you bring us safe to the village your life shall be spared and you shall come with us and take a share in the treasure we mean to capture from your rich English abbeys and churches. How say you, men? Is that a bargain?"

"Aye," they growled. "If you say so, Thorvald."

Edgar hesitated. "I—I should be betraying my own people if I did," he muttered.

"Your people will be dead, and in a day or two you will be far away. In a week or two you will be rich."

He hesitated again. "The—the channel is difficult. I cannot be sure of finding it. If I fail to find it you will kill me."

"We shall not kill you for doing your best. It is only if you refuse or if you attempt to betray us or trick us that we shall kill you. Come, boy, make up your mind. Will you do your best for us, or will you be killed now? It is all one to me, for we shall find our own way if you will not show us, though we may take longer over it."

The steersman had drawn his sword. Edgar knew he meant

The steersman had drawn his sword. Edgar knew he meant what he said.

what he said. He had only to refuse, and his head would be off in an instant. Thorvald would make no more of killing him than he would of killing a cockroach.

"I will do my best," he said. "I shall need to go right into the prow so that I can see when the water is too shallow."

He was praying that the delay had been long enough for the village people to drive the cattle away. The ship had been almost stopped for a long while now, for the men were not rowing and there was scarcely wind to fill the sail. Moreover, the tide was beginning to ebb out of the river. If anything the ship must be moving astern.

Thorvald bade the man Olaf take him to the prow and guard him.

"At a sign of treachery, off with his head!" Thorvald commanded. "And if he is slow at seeing the twists of the channel prick him with your knife to quicken his eyesight."

The big man chuckled and drew his knife. He pricked Edgar with it then and there as a sample, and the boy bit his lip to prevent a cry of pain.

The men began to row easily, and the ship forged slowly ahead over the ebbing tide. One of the oarsmen, on Thorvald's instructions, took a long pole with measurements marked on it and began testing the depth of water with it.

Thorvald gripped the tiller attached to the big steering oar and altered course as Edgar instructed.

"To starboard now! Steer for the great tree there! Now to larboard! More! Let her come round to bring those two clumps of bushes in line. Now—steady!"

The ship zigzagged from shore to shore, covering a great distance. It progressed infinitely slowly toward the village, which still could only be seen by the smoke from its two or three peat fires. The roofs of the low thatched cottages were still hidden by the bushes and trees. The village had indeed been built so that it would not be easily visible from the estuary, but the people had become careless about their fires through the years of peace.

The man with the pole, sounding constantly, reported ample water for the ship, and Thorvald was satisfied. He could not know that all this zigzagging was quite unnecessary, that in fact there was ample water for the ship everywhere as yet, and that his young pilot was doing his best to waste time, and more time, to let the village people get away.

But Edgar knew well that this pretense could not last much longer. Soon the ship would really be in shallow water. Soon he would have to pilot her in good earnest.

Suddenly he saw ahead the very slight change in the color of the water which indicated a bank. "Starboard!" he cried sharply, and Thorvald thrust the tiller over and at the same time ordered the starboard oars to rest so that the larboard ones would pull the ship around.

The man with the pole touched the mud bank and grunted that it had been a close shave. Olaf pricked Edgar's ribs with his knife to warn him to be smarter next time. Edgar clapped his hand to his side instinctively, and felt blood warm and sticky on his fingers. Olaf chuckled.

"Now steady for the oak tree there," Edgar muttered through clenched teeth, and Olaf repeated the instruction for Thorvald to hear while at the same time pricking Edgar afresh.

"Louder, young cock! Let us have your orders so we can hear them, or not at all!"

Edgar groaned, not because of the pain, but because the first of the cottages had come into view.

There could be no direct approach for the ship, however. The tide was ebbing fast and in one or two places the mud was beginning to show. If the ship was to remain afloat she must be kept exactly in the deep channel.

Then he saw how the tide was sluicing across a bank on a sharp bend, and he saw his chance. The bank could not be seen.

"There!" he cried to Thorvald. "You see how the tide runs through the channel? We must have all the speed we can get to go through, or we shall be swept onto the mud!"

Thorvald nodded in understanding. "Pull!" he cried to the men. "Put down the pole, Jurgens, and take your oar! You too, Olaf! Make her jump now!"

The ship leaped forward. Edgar could not help admiring the way she responded to the men's sudden effort. She was like a thing of life—like a mettlesome horse leaping at the touch of spurs. The men groaned, the oars bent, but the ship seemed almost to laugh.

Straight for the sluicing tide rip she went—and straight for the mud bank it concealed.

Too late Thorvald saw what Edgar had done.

"Treachery!" he roared, and flung a spear.

The spear hissed through the air and stood quivering in the woodwork of the prow just where Edgar had been standing a moment ago, but he was there no longer.

Straight and true, with all the power of the oars and sail to give her speed, the ship ran onto the mud, slid up it, dug her forefront in, and stopped.

The men were in complete confusion. Some had stopped rowing when Thorvald shouted and flung the spear. Some found their oars scraping mud. Others were caught in the act of putting full weight onto their oars and were thrown from their benches. Some oars snapped. Some were forced sharply back against the ship's sides so that their inboard ends beat the oarsmen like clubs.

Thorvald, cursing them all and cursing Edgar more than them, stormed his way forward. Some of the men joined him and two jumped overboard onto the mud, but their own weight and the weight of their armor and weapons caused them to stagger helplessly and sink to their thighs.

Edgar had plunged into the mud, too, but he was used to it

and knew which way to turn to find deep water. By the time the first men came to look for him he was swimming strongly toward the land.

"Shoot him!" Thorvald raved. "A pot of gold to the man who hits him!"

It was hopeless. Their bows were stowed in the arms chest under the poop and had no strings fitted. A few men scrambled to get them. Others contented themselves with throwing spears.

Olaf growled, "It would be better to get the ship afloat, Thorvald. The tide is ebbing."

That was common sense, and Thorvald ordered them to leave the boy and attend to the ship.

They had to get the sail off her, for that was holding her fast against the mud. They had to unship the forward oars and use them as poles to push her off the mud. But with the oars aft, where the ship was still fairly deep in water, they tried to row.

By the time they were ready for a concerted effort the tide had fallen to such an extent that one-third of the ship was clear of the water altogether.

"Then lift her off!" Thorvald shouted. "Are you men? Have I shipped seamen or children?"

They stripped off their armor and weapons and jumped overboard. They struggled and slipped and fell. There was no holding ground in the mud at all, and the more they heaved against the ship the further down their bodies sank.

At last they gave up sulkily and crawled back into the ship to face the curses of their leader, but they were too exhausted to care. Some of them growled angrily that it had been his fault for trusting the boy.

The bank on which they were stranded was now revealed by the tide—an elliptical island of mud around which the deep channel divided. They could get ashore, but only by swimming and wading through the mud; or they could rest on board till the tide rose again, in twelve hours' time, to float the ship off.

"We'll wait," said Olaf the bow man. "The village will still be there tomorrow."

"But the cattle will not, nor the people!" Thorvald thundered. "By Odin, do you think burning their houses will satisfy me? I want to kill them—every man, woman and child!"

The men sat hunched on their benches and scowled at him. They were free men, not his slaves. He was their leader, but he had failed them. What did they care about his revenge?

So they sat while Edgar scrambled ashore and ran to the cover of some windswept gorse bushes. He was out of range of their spears now, but not of arrows; therefore he paused only long enough to make sure the ship was truly fast and that they were not yet swarming ashore, and ran again.

As he ran with head down and body bent, swerving from side to side, he feared all the while to feel an arrow pierce between his shoulders. But none came, and when he again looked back he saw that the Norsemen were down in the mud struggling to lift the ship.

Thus he came presently to his father's farmstead and the mud-walled cottages of the villeins, and sighed with relief to find them deserted. Even the hens which usually scratched about their doors seemed to have been carried off.

He ran on further, knowing which way his people would have gone. Then suddenly he stopped at the edge of a thicket as men broke from it in all directions and surrounded him.

He stared wildly for a moment at the spears and swords in their hands, the bows slung on their backs, the long knives naked at their belts. And then he saw his father.

"Father! These men——"

"Edgar! Alstan said you had gone to meet the pirates."

"I did, Father! They made me pilot the ship into the river, but I led them onto the Tongue bank. She is fast there now, and they were trying to get her off when I last saw them. But the tide is falling and they will not. But—but these men——"

"King Edward's men, Edgar—a hundred of them marching southward to Maldon and thirsting for work to do. Eh, lads, do you hear? The pirates are stranded aboard their ship in the river! Shall we teach them who rules in England now?"

"Aye!" they shouted. "Lead the way, Thane! We're ready for them!"

"Go to your mother, boy," Edgar's father commanded him. "She did not expect to see you again. This is men's work."

"But Father, if you would let me come——"

"I will not. You have done your share. Back to your mother as I tell you!"

So Edgar went reluctantly, and that evening he and Alstan climbed a tree to watch the flames rising from a great fire in the river. The pirate ship was being burned. The village, for a while at least, was safe.

The Vikings

THE VIKINGS were the greatest open-boat travelers the world
has ever known. Clad in skins, armed with spears and swords,
rigging a tent over the boat for shelter at night, they not only
went wherever water would take them, but they established
colonies and trading routes and conquered great nations.

From Norway, Sweden and Denmark they navigated the
northern seas amid ice and fog, and found Iceland. Their de-
scendants live there today. And from Iceland they went on to
Greenland, and from there to America five hundred years before Columbus found it.

They swarmed down the coasts of Europe, sacked London
and Paris and a score of other cities; they went into the Mediterranean and down to the coast of Africa. They set a Danish
king, Canute, on the throne of England; they forced the king
of France to give them the great province of Normandy; they
occupied and ruled much of Holland and Germany.

From the Baltic they took their long-ships down the great
Russian rivers, rolling them on logs overland from one river

to another, and so reached the Black Sea and the Caspian. They set up trading posts and fortresses all through Russia, and their colonists founded the present Russian nation. Their chieftains became czars and emperors.

They attacked Constantinople but could not conquer it. But the emperor who then ruled there was so impressed with them that he enlisted them into a famous regiment called the Varangian Guard, which lasted for about three hundred years.

The Viking chieftain's most treasured possession was his ship. Therefore when a chieftain died, his followers did their best to send his ship to Valhalla with him. Sometimes they built a great funeral pyre and burned him in the ship, with his weapons, dogs and even slaves. At other times they merely buried the ship under a huge cairn of earth and stones, without burning it.

Some of these buried ships have been found, and one is preserved in the museum of Oslo in Norway. Thus we are able to see exactly how such a ship was built, rigged and sailed. In fact we know more about this ship, of about A.D. 900, than we do about most other ships down past the time of the *Mayflower*, whose "replica," *Mayflower II*, had to be built from records of ships of that period. However, this frail craft was actually sailed across the Atlantic in 1957, over three hundred years after the Pilgrims made their courageous 67-day voyage from Plymouth, England to what is now Plymouth, Massachusetts.

Other famous old ships that, like the Viking ship, are actually preserved today include "Old Ironsides"—the famous frigate *Constitution*, originally launched in 1797 and now berthed in the Navy Yard at Boston, Massachusetts, and Lord Nelson's famous ship *Victory,* on view at Portsmouth, England.

Black Ivory

THE PORTUGUESE RESIDENT was a charming man. He was delighted to receive as guests on his island the captain and crew of Her Majesty's brig *Skipper*. The entire island was at their disposal. Did they want fruit? Fresh meat? Water? It was all theirs!

Lieutenant Ramble, R. N., in command of the *Skipper*, thanked him but said dryly, "What I really require is information about the slave trade."

The Portuguese Resident raised his eyebrows in shocked surprise. "Slave trade? My dear captain, are you suggesting——?"

"I am not suggesting anything," Lieutenant Ramble retorted curtly. "I am merely asking you for information. We know that considerable numbers of slaves are being shipped from this part of Africa to the West Indies. We have been patroling the mainland coast for months past without result. Now we are turning our attention to the islands. Can you help us?"

The Portuguese Resident shrugged his shoulders, spread his hands and showed his teeth in an expansive smile. "This is a small island, Captain. The entire population would scarcely make one cargo for a slave trader! How can I help you?"

Lieutenant Ramble sighed. It did indeed look as though he must search elsewhere. He knew well enough that the population of the island was small. Slaves—"black ivory" as they were called—were rounded up far inland by Arab traders and brought down to the coast for shipment overseas. In the West Indies plantation owners were still willing to buy them, and the fact that most civilized countries had now made the slave trade illegal had only sent the price up. Huge profits were to be made by men willing to take the risks involved.

Her Majesty's brig *Skipper* and a score of other small ships like her were doing their best to stop the traffic by capturing the slave ships on the high seas. But the slave ships were fast and their captains clever. It would be so much more effective to discover the depots on the coast from which the slaves were shipped.

Lieutenant Ramble looked at the island from the deck of his ship anchored in the bay, and was not impressed. It appeared to contain one house—the official Residence with the Portuguese flag flying above it—and a collection of mud huts. Beyond the point, in another small bay, a Spanish ship was lying.

"What is she doing here?" asked Lieutenant Ramble.

The Resident shrugged again. "We have a little trade—copra, some fruit, dried fish. Also we ourselves need supplies. It is natural that ships should call here sometimes."

Yes, that was true. On the other hand the Spanish ship did not look quite like a local trader. Her tall masts showed above the land, above the palm trees. She could carry a great deal of canvas. And the trim of her yards and rigging gave her almost the look of a man-of-war. She had smartness, and a well-disciplined and efficient crew. It was unusual in an African coastal trader of any nationality.

Lieutenant Ramble said nothing, but privately he made up his mind to watch that ship.

He could do nothing about her now. He was a guest in a foreign port. He could not demand the right to search her— but once she was out on the high seas matters would be different.

Meanwhile the Portuguese Resident was becoming even more charming.

"Captain, there is little my poor island can offer in the way of entertainment, but if you and your officers would care to have dinner with me this evening . . . ?"

Lieutenant Ramble hesitated for a moment and then accepted. It would be churlish to refuse, and over dinner he might get the man talking. He was sure the Resident knew more than he had so far said about black ivory.

"Thank you. We shall be delighted. There will be, I think, only two of us—myself and my master's mate, Mr. Waring."

The Resident raised his eyebrows again. "Two only? Do you have no more than two officers, then?"

Lieutenant Ramble smiled. "I did not include my two midshipmen, who are only boys. They will remain on board in charge of the ship."

In the background the two midshipmen exchanged scowls. Only boys, indeed! Why, Lowndes, who had been at sea almost two years, was nearly sixteen, and Kirk, who had been in the service more than a year, was only a few months younger.

H.M.S. Skipper was in fact a very small ship, only seventy feet long and carrying but three guns—one thirty-two pounder carronade on each side by way of broadside, and a long swiveling "chaser" in the bows. Her crew consisted of the captain, Lieutenant Ramble, the master's mate, Mr. Waring—a young man only two years older than the senior midshipman, the two midshipmen, a boatswain's mate and some forty seamen and miscellaneous ratings. A fair proportion of these last were native Africans.

As soon as the Portuguese Resident had gone ashore Lieutenant Ramble called his second-in-command. "Waring, take the cutter around the point and see what you can make of that Spaniard. Don't go in too close. I don't want him to think we are suspicious. Try to look as though you are just exercising the crew."

The master's mate nodded and a few minutes later the boat was pulling smartly away with eight men at the oars. Two hours later it was back.

"She's a slaver all right. I'll stake a month's pay on it. And she's armed. I should say she carries at least six guns."

"Humph," said Lieutenant Ramble. "About what I thought. All right, as soon as this confounded dinner party is over we'll get out to sea and wait for her. But I wish we could board her now!"

"Aye—but I don't think we'd find anything if we did. She seems to be flying light. Not an ounce of cargo of any sort in her, I should say. But I'll tell you what else I noticed. In a grove of palm trees ashore, just beyond her, there are some big huts— long low buildings, like warehouses. If we could find out what is in them we should know something, I'm thinking!"

Lieutenant Ramble stared thoughtfully toward the point behind which the Spanish vessel lay at anchor.

"Yes," he murmured. "You know, I've been suspicious ever since the Resident insisted on our anchoring in this bay instead of the other. More shelter indeed! I'm convinced he just wanted to keep us out of the other bay, and for some good reason. Well, we'll tackle him about those huts this evening. Meantime— I have it! Lowndes, do you feel like doing a little spying?"

The senior midshipman grinned. "I'm game, sir! Do you mean for me to have a look at those huts?"

"I do. You'll be taking us ashore in the cutter tonight. As soon as you've landed us, pull offshore as though you meant to return to the ship, but when you're out of view from the beach—it'll be dark by then and you won't be seen more than a hundred yards —pull down to the point instead. Land this side of it and cross the spit of land on foot. Make sure you aren't seen by the Spaniard. Think you can manage it?"

"Aye, sir! And then?"

"Return to the ship and come ashore for us when you see our signal. I'll flash a light of some sort."

"Very good, sir."

"And if you are caught make up some sort of story. Say you were fishing, or something, and went ashore by accident."

"Aye, sir. I'll think up something."

That left Midshipman Kirk rather less pleased than before. He would be left on board alone.

"You'll be in charge of the ship!" Lowndes consoled him. "Think of the honor!"

Midshipman Kirk aimed a kick at him and missed.

There was a light offshore breeze when Lowndes took the cutter in that evening with his superior officers. They were in full uniform and welcomed the breeze for the relieving coolness it brought.

"Must keep up appearances," Lieutenant Ramble growled as he adjusted his dress sword on taking his seat in the boat. "I'd rather be doing your job though, young Lowndes!"

Lowndes grinned cheerfully, and hoped they would have an enjoyable dinner.

He landed his passengers and noted how quickly they passed out of sight as they walked up the beach. The darkness of the shore had the effect of hiding things much more than on the water. Nevertheless he took the boat back almost to the ship before turning toward the point. The boat was a good mile from the beach as he rowed along the coast.

When he at last turned shoreward he bade the men row gently. The sound of oars, he knew, could be heard for a great distance. And when he could see the beach clearly again he told them to cease rowing altogether. So the boat drifted in and grounded almost without making a sound.

He waded ashore, carrying his shoes, but put them on again when once ashore. He had half a mile to walk over unknown ground and through dense undergrowth. His feet would be cut to pieces if he tried to go barefoot, and that might cripple him altogether.

Feeling his way, taking direction by the stars, he moved cautiously across the narrow spit of land which divided the two anchorages. But soon he could see the masts and spars of the Spanish ship standing sharply outlined against the purple sky.

He turned inland in order to come to the huts, which he could not yet see, though he could see the palm trees which screened them. And then he came to a sudden halt. There were men on the beach, and lights moving about.

He crouched in the undergrowth, watching and listening. He could not understand what was said, but gradually he realized what was happening. Several boats—big lighters or rafts—were being loaded. They could only be going off to the Spanish ship. And now he saw that the Spaniard's sails had been loosed and were hanging from the yards ready to be set. He could hear the canvas slapping lazily in the gentle breeze.

Why should she be sailing at night like this? Why load cargo secretly by torchlight? He *must* find out what that cargo was.

He crept closer, bending low, darting from bush to bush. And at last he saw. A long line of dark figures, apparently tied together in a human chain, was being coaxed and driven from the direction of the huts down to the beach, onto the lighters and out to the slave ship. Black ivory being loaded! And this was the depot for which they had been searching!

He waited for no more. He turned and crept back, but as

soon as he had reached the ridge of the land he broke into a run. Forgetting to take off his shoes he plunged straight into the water and scrambled back into the cutter.

He gasped orders as the ready hands pulled him in. "Back together! Pull starboard, back port! Now, together—pull! Back to the ship—and put everything you've got into it!"

As soon as the cutter came alongside he sprang from it and flung himself on board the *Skipper*.

"Kirk, the Spaniard! She's loading slaves now and means to sail immediately! Her sails are bent already! Take the cutter ashore and tell Lieutenant Ramble. Tell them I'll be getting the ship ready for sea."

"But dash it, Bob, you were supposed to take the cutter ashore! I can get the ship ready!"

"Don't argue. I'm senior, and this is an order. And don't waste time, man!"

Kirk went over the side and the cutter pulled away with him. Before he was well clear Lowndes was giving orders to the boatswain's mate.

"I want all hands on deck and the ship put ready for sailing the moment the captain comes on board. That ship in the other anchorage is a slaver and will be sailing at any moment. We must put to sea in chase of her. Do you understand?"

"Aye sir! Do you want the cable hove short?"

"Yes, of course. Bring the anchor almost apeak. Loose the gaskets and see all the gear free. Have the sweeps handy. We may need them to get clear."

The sweeps were four oars intended for rowing the ship if necessary in a calm. Each required two men to pull it.

Soon the ship was in a bustle of activity. The capstan was manned and the cable hove in till the anchor was barely resting on the bottom. The sails were loosed from the yards and hung idly flapping.

Lowndes paced the deck in a fever of anxiety. Where was the

cutter? Why didn't the captain come? Was that worm of a Resident deliberately delaying him? Had Kirk lost his way in the darkness?

He swarmed aloft and tried with the night glasses to see what the Spaniard was doing, but he could only just make out her topsails beyond the point without being able to see whether she was under way or not.

He returned to the deck, where the men now had everything ready, and issued more orders.

"Captains of guns, see everything ready for action! That ship over there is armed, and we mean to take her. Shot the bow chaser, but have the carronades loaded with grape. And have small arms ready in case it comes to boarding."

That done, he fretted again. Oh, where was the captain? Why didn't they come? He searched the sea for the cutter, but could see nothing. He ran aloft again, but could see nothing of the boat from the masthead either. And then he turned the glasses toward the point—and almost dropped them. He could not see the Spaniard either!

A frantic search—and then he saw her. She was standing out, dim and ghostly, beyond the point. She had sailed!

He looked hastily for the cutter again. Then he slid down to the deck and snapped his orders almost before he touched.

"Man the capstan! Bring the anchor to the cathead and secure! Sheet home jib and fore-topsail as soon as the anchor's aweigh!"

"Are you taking her to sea, sir?" the boatswain's mate inquired, respectfully enough but somewhat doubtfully.

"Yes, I am. It's either that or lose the slaver. Don't look so confoundedly glum, Bates! I know what I'm doing."

"Yes, sir. That's it, lads! Heave away then!"

"And Bates, make sure the sternlight's burning bright and clear. The cutter can follow that when she comes out."

"Aye, sir. Anchor's aweigh now, sir. She's paying off to starboard, looks like, sir."

"Let her come. Port the helm! Sheet home t'gallants and main-topsail! And send a man aloft to watch the slaver!"

The men obeyed promptly. His excitement had spread to them. They were going to sea—going into action after many weeks of fruitless cruising and waiting. There was only a mid-shipman in command, but that did not matter.

The anchor was stowed at the cathead and lashed to keep it from swinging against the bow. The ship was dressed with canvas once more and the sails were drawing—not strongly, for the wind was very light, but sufficiently well to take the ship away from the anchorage.

"She's setting everything she's got, sir!" the man aloft reported. "Standing away to the southwest, by the look of her!"

Lowndes ordered more canvas to be set on the brig. Normally she was a fast ship, but in these light airs she was not at her best, being heavily built like any man-of-war.

His only consolation was that the Spaniard was heavily loaded and would have no more wind than the brig.

"Drawing away from us, sir, I reckon!" came the voice from aloft, and Lowndes bit his fingernails impatiently. He would certainly look like a fool if she did get away after all!

"Out sweeps!" he cried. "If we can't catch her sailing we'll try pulling!"

It passed through his mind that the more speed they made the more difficult it would be for Lieutenant Ramble in the cutter to overtake them. But he had committed himself now. He must succeed—or die in the attempt! Afterward—well, let afterward take care of itself.

And after half an hour's strenuous pulling at the great sweeps his heart leaped as the lookout called down from the masthead, "We're making up on her now, sir!"

He wondered if the slaver's crew had seen the brig. Did they know they were being chased? Would they too produce sweeps when they realized it? Or would they rely on being able to fight their way clear?

Presently he could see the Spaniard clearly enough from the deck, and he called the lookout down. It was difficult to estimate the distance, but he thought the two ships could be scarcely more than half a mile apart now, with the brig slowly drawing abeam of the Spaniard.

"Can you see her?" he asked the captain of the forward gun. "Can you put a shot across her bows, do you think?"

"Aye sir—or into her hull if you want!"

"No!" Lowndes snapped. "Whatever happens I don't want to put anything through her hull. We'd only kill the poor devils of slaves that way. We'll shoot at her rigging if it comes to a fight. But first I want a shot across her bows to make her heave to. Fire when you're ready."

"Very good, sir."

The gun roared out, and a spout of water just ahead of the Spaniard showed where the shot had fallen.

"Now we'll see what she does," Lowndes murmured.

The result was unexpected. A flash appeared aboard the slaver, followed almost immediately by the roar of a gun, and a shot tore through the brig's foresail, leaving a ragged hole.

For a second Lowndes gaped at it in amazement. The Spaniard had dared to open fire! And he, Midshipman Robert Lowndes, not yet sixteen years of age, was committed to taking his ship into action! For that one second the enormity of it all almost overwhelmed him. What on earth would Lieutenant Ramble have to say about it? What would My Lords of the Admiralty have to say?

Then he thrust such thoughts aside.

"Starboard a bit!" he ordered the helmsman. "Stand by to fire, for'ard there! Aim at her foremast!"

"Aye, sir! Ready now, sir!"

"Fire!"

They waited a breathless moment—then a cheer went up from for'ard. The Spaniard's fore-topsail had come down with a run. Lowndes found himself cheering madly—but he checked himself quickly. He was the captain now. He must behave himself! And a moment later he did not feel like cheering. The Spaniard had opened with her broadside—four guns, by the look of things. The little brig quivered as a shot struck her; there was a splintering of wood, and a man cried out sharply.

"What happened? Is anyone hurt?"

A tense voice replied, "Nothing much, sir. One of the sweeps smashed and a man gashed with a splinter. He'll be all right."

"Very well. In sweeps! She'll carry her way now. I'm laying the ship alongside her. Fire when your sights bear, port! Aim at her rigging, mind!"

The port gun roared as the two ships closed. Small grapeshot peppered the slaver, cutting her sails and rigging. From somewhere aboard her a man screamed.

"Reload and fire as soon as you can," Lowndes ordered grimly. "Stand by, boarding party!"

The broadside came again from the Spaniard, and again the little brig quivered. Again there was a splintering of wood, and again a man cried out. But this time the cry was followed quickly by a voice explaining sheepishly, "It's all right, sir. Nobody hurt. I was holding a bit of the bulwarks, and suddenly it wasn't there! Gave me a shock, like!"

In fact several feet of the brig's bulwarks had been splintered. Midshipman Lowndes groaned as he saw the damage. But this was no time for groaning, any more than cheering.

A second volley of grapeshot poured over the Spaniard's decks. Her jib came down, its halyards cut, and smothered the bowsprit. Dragging in the water, it had the effect of bringing the slaver almost to a standstill, and at the same time swinging her head around. With sudden and frightening rapidity the two ships seemed to rush together.

Seconds later their spars crashed together, and then their hulls.

"Follow me, lads!" cried Lowndes, and leaped for the Spaniard's rail followed by some twenty of his men.

He could see nothing clearly in the darkness. Figures appeared and vanished. A sword flashed past his face, but he did not see the man who had wielded it. He was only dimly aware of someone writhing under his feet as he rushed on. Behind him there was a confusion of firing, clashing steel, tearing woodwork.

Someone who might have been the slaver's captain—he wore a uniform of sorts—appeared before him. Lowndes hurled himself at the figure and the man went down.

Then a hand caught at his shoulder and held him back, and the voice of the boatswain's mate said gruffly, "Easy, sir, easy! He's surrendering!"

Midshipman Lowndes gasped. "I got carried away! Do you mean we've taken her, Bates?"

"Near enough, sir. We've taken this end of her, anyway."

"This end? What do you mean? What's happening for'ard?"

"The ships swung apart again before the for'ard boarding party could follow us. We're on our own. What with casualties and so on there's not more than a dozen of us, and there's thirty or more Spaniards licking their wounds on the foredeck. They'll be at us again presently."

And now Lowndes could see how things were. His men stood around him—he counted eighteen, of whom at least six were obviously wounded. And *H.M.S. Skipper* was a good hundred yards away.

"Sweeps!" he shouted. "Pull your starboard sweeps, you fools! Oh, isn't there anyone aboard her with any sense? Shout, Bates! Your voice'll carry better than mine."

The boatswain's mate shouted with a voice which was customarily heard above the noise of gales. "Dickson! Smith! Johnson! Get her alongside again! Pull starboard sweeps!"

"Let 'em have it!" cried Lowndes, and fired his pistol in their midst, following it by rushing at them with his cutlass.

Someone close beside Lowndes muttered curtly, "They're coming! Look out, boys!"

It was the Spaniards who were coming. They were sneaking along from the foredeck, hoping to take the intruders by surprise.

"Let 'em have it!" cried Lowndes, and fired his pistol into their midst, following it by rushing at them with his cutlass.

Something struck him on the head and he went down. Something fell on top of him and pinned him down. Then feet trampled on him and over him, until at last he passed into blissful unconsciousness.

He awoke to hear a voice crying, "Here's Mr. Lowndes! Here he is, sir! I've found him!"

Then, astonishingly, he was looking up into the face of Lieutenant Ramble, and someone was holding a lantern.

"You're alive! You don't deserve to be, you young fool! What the deuce d'you mean by running away with my ship?"

Lowndes managed to sit up with a struggle. His head felt as if a cannonball had struck it, and every bone in his body ached.

"I'm sorry, sir! I—I waited as long as I could, but the Spaniard was sailing! Is it all right? Have we taken her? Did—did we lose many men?"

"We've taken her—though I'm not sure we would have if Waring and I hadn't come up with reinforcements in the nick of time. Your men were going down like ninepins, with three Spaniards to each one of them. We're sorting out the casualties now. Two killed and a dozen or so wounded seems to be the sum of it, including yourself."

"I'm not wounded, sir! I only fell down!"

Lieutenant Ramble laughed. "You'll have a scar on your head for the rest of your life to show for it, anyway!"

"Will—will I be court-martialed for it, sir?"

Lieutenant Ramble laughed again. "No—not by the time I've cooked up a suitable report. You ought to be, of course, but we seldom get our deserts in this life."

"Thank you, sir! And—what about the slaves?"

"Four hundred odd of them, frightened out of their wits. We're taking 'em back to the island for the time being. The ship'll have to be patched up before we can sail her to Free-town. You made a mess of her, young man."

"I know, sir. And—what will happen to that Portuguese Resi-dent?"

"Humph. Well, our dinner party was interrupted, so now we're going back to have breakfast with him. And I should guess that he won't have much appetite!"

The *Cutty Sark*

O<small>NE</small> <small>AFTERNOON</small> in 1913 a British seaman strolling along the waterfront at New Orleans saw a battered old sailing ship flying the Portuguese flag. She was called the *Ferreira*.

There were not many big sailing ships left even then, and this one was obviously a real old-timer. Moreover she had the fine lines and tall spars of a clipper. The visitor was interested. What ship had she been before she became the *Ferreira?*

Nobody aboard the ship could speak English. The skipper, who was sitting on the poop patching a sail, indicated by signs that the visitor could inspect the ship if he wished. So he did, and became more and more curious.

The names over her cabin doors were in English; her old British official number was still there, and her tonnage markings.

But her old name—that was nowhere; not on her bows, nor her stern, nor her wheel, nor her bell.

Then, when he had almost given up, the visitor found a second bell, right up for'ard on her fo'c'sle. It was heavily coated with silver paint, but the visitor's searching fingers detected something under the paint. Quickly, risking the anger of the Portuguese skipper, he took out his pocket knife and began to scrape. The paint flaked away. A date appeared—1869—the year the ship was launched.

Thoroughly excited now, he scraped again—and slowly the name was revealed, one of the most famous names in British sailing history—*Cutty Sark*.

That was in 1913, and afterward the old ship sailed for her Portuguese owners all through the 1914–18 war. Then, in 1922, she was bought back by an Englishman, Captain Dowman, and when he died she was given to the Thames Nautical Training College for training cadets. Finally she was restored to her original condition—the condition she was in when she held pride of place as the queen of British tea clippers—and was safely berthed in permanent drydock at Greenwich, England, where she may be seen today, her beautiful spars rising high above the river.

The *Cutty Sark* was a later, Scottish-built model of the famous clipper ships, first designed and built in the United States by Donald McKay and others in the 1840's and 1850's, when the California Gold Rush put the speed of these slim graceful craft at a premium. McKay's most famous clipper, *The Flying Cloud,* was built with characteristic slender hull and sharp bow, and probably carried more than 8,000 yards of canvas. In a run from New York to San Francisco around Cape Horn she made the customary 150-day trip in eighty-nine days!

But of all these American-built flying ships that once swept the seas from here to China, it seems that not one remains in the

United States today. However, two British clippers, the *Star of India* and the *Balclutha,* that later served under the American flag, have been restored at San Diego and at San Francisco, respectively.

Still another kind of famous sailing ship may be seen today at Mystic, Connecticut—the whaler *Charles W. Morgan.* Built in 1841, this broad-beamed veteran took more whales in her thirty-seven voyages than any other whaleship in the old American sailing fishery.

For Services Rendered

🏴

🏴

🏴

🏴

🏴

SHIP RIGHT AHEAD, SIR!" young Pickering, the junior cadet aboard the *S.S. Hopewell,* reported to the chief officer. And then, not quite as certainly, "It—it looks like a submarine!"

The chief officer, raising his binoculars, said nothing. It would not be a submarine, of course, here in the southwestern corner of the Caribbean Sea, but what was it? A long low dark shape on the sea, scarcely to be seen at all amid the heaving of the swell which the hurricane had left in its wake.

But suddenly he saw what it was, and called excitedly to the captain, "It's a derelict, sir! I think it's that coaster we heard was sinking!"

Two days ago, while the *Hopewell* was struggling through the tail end of a hurricane, a wireless message had been received from an American steamer. She was taking off the crew from a small motor vessel said to be in danger of sinking. The position given was right on the *Hopewell's* course.

"By Jove," the chief officer muttered, "if we had come on it an hour or two later we might have run slap into it! You'd never see that in the dark."

As they drew nearer to it they could see that the main deck of the little ship was almost awash. Only the raised fo'c'sle and poop stood clear of the water, with a squat exhaust funnel aft and a tiny wheelhouse.

"But she didn't sink after all!" the chief officer exclaimed. "By Jove, that's pluck for you!"

They all felt that. The crew had abandoned her, yet the ship refused to sink. After two days, here she was, still afloat. That she was now a danger to shipping was not her fault.

"I suppose," the chief officer murmured hesitantly, "I suppose you wouldn't try towing her, sir? We're only a hundred miles from Santa Barbara."

The *Hopewell* was bound for the little port of Santa Barbara to load a cargo of sugar. She was late, having been delayed many hours by the hurricane, and the chief engineer was already complaining that his engines did not like hurrying.

"They need verra careful nursing," he had told the captain. "Ye'll ken they're not so young as they were, Captain."

There was another factor to be considered. The weather was by no means settled yet. After the hurricane, had come a hot stifling calm, with heavy black clouds lowering to the horizon. They threatened rain—intense tropical rain which can delay a ship as much as dense fog.

The captain considered all these things as he frowned at the pathetic little ship lying derelict. It was a pity to leave her there to sink eventually, or perhaps to be taken in tow by someone else. And yet . . .

"She might be worth quite a bit of salvage money," the chief officer reminded him. "She looks like a modern type, and if she's full of cargo . . ."

"All right," said the captain abruptly. "We'll at least have a look at her. Take the launch across, and an engineer, and let me have a report. And be quick. If we're to do anything, it must be before dark—and before that rain comes."

The afternoon peace aboard the *Hopewell* vanished swiftly. Sailors who had finished work for the day—so they thought—came grumbling, but running, to get the launch ready. The engineer on watch sprang to action as the telegraph jangled. The chief engineer came puffing up the bridge ladder to inquire what all the commotion was about.

The three cadets dashed for their oilskins—in case the rain came—and armed themselves with flashlights. They were to be the crew of the launch. Flashlights would be necessary for inspecting the derelict, for the light was fading already.

Nobody grumbled seriously. If the derelict could be saved everybody would get a share of the salvage money, from captain to cabin boy.

"How much do you think we'll get?" Slim Roberts—always optimistic—inquired.

Jumbo White, the senior cadet, grinned cheerfully. "Oh about fourpence, I should say. The owners get the biggest share, then the skipper, and so on down the scale. It might pay for a bar of chocolate, I suppose."

Roberts scowled and threw his sneaker at him.

Five minutes later the launch was being lowered, with her crew already in her. Under the chief officer's guidance she was lowered slowly, then dropped swiftly onto the crest of a rising wave. The patent hooks were released in an instant, and as she fell with the wave her motor burst into life and she was steered away from the ship's side.

"Just a quick inspection first," the chief officer told the second engineer. "Then we'll come back and report. The main thing is to find out if she's still making water, or if there's a chance of getting her pumps going and keeping her afloat."

The launch crossed the half-mile of sea between the two ships

and ran in under the derelict's stern. They read the name—
Empresa, Panama.

"That's the name the American ship reported," the chief
officer told them. "It's a miracle, no less!"

And when they came to examine the ship they all agreed that
it was.

Skylights were smashed, doors gone, portholes burst open,
ventilators flattened, the exhaust funnel battered out of shape,
sections of rail uprooted and twisted beyond recognition. The
little wheelhouse leaned drunkenly and the one mast was broken
and hanging over the side.

"She'll be flooded down below," the second engineer said—
and he was right. Wherever they shone their flashlights they saw
the light reflected in water, or heard it swishing about if they
could not see it.

The second engineer had brought an assistant with him, a
young Scots junior named Angus Duncan. These two climbed
through the broken engine room skylight and disappeared while
the chief officer, White and Pickering explored the rest of the
ship. Roberts had been left in charge of the launch, much to
his annoyance.

A few minutes later they gathered again on the poop—all
except Angus Duncan.

"He's clearing one of the pumps," the second engineer explained. "There's a dandy little auxiliary diesel engine for working them, and I'm pretty sure we can get it going. He can stay
while we go back to report."

"Then the lads had better stay with him," said the chief officer.
"Nothing much can happen in the few minutes we shall be
away, I suppose. Roberts can go down below and give him a
hand. He's quite a good amateur engineer."

"The point is," said the second engineer, "she doesn't seem
to be leaking. I couldn't hear water coming in anywhere. What's
on board now must all have come down from above."

The chief officer agreed. "The sooner we can get a towrope out the better. Right now, you're in charge, White. You can occupy your time searching the captain's cabin and chartroom for papers or anything else worth saving. Okay, Second, let's go."

They jumped down into the launch, and Roberts came aboard, though not very pleased at being told he was now an assistant engineer.

However, he only grumbled, "Oh well, I suppose it's all in the day's work!"—and lowered himself gingerly through the engine room skylight.

White and Pickering went down the narrow companionway to the captain's and officers' cabins.

"It's the only time you're likely to be allowed in a captain's cabin," White told his junior, "so make the most of it, young Pickles."

Actually it was such a tiny cabin that it could scarcely contain the two of them together.

"What's that in the bunk?" asked White, and Pickering passed him a large sodden sheet of paper. Everything was sodden— bed, clothing, floor and furniture.

"Gosh, it's the chart! That's a queer place to keep it—in his bunk. Do you think he did his navigation lying down?"

White shone his flashlight on it. "It might tell us where she was bound," he said, and pointed to a faint pencil line, blurred by salt water. "Yes, there's the course line. I suppose it goes to Santa Barbara. No, it doesn't! I say, that's dashed peculiar! It doesn't go anywhere in particular."

They peered at it together, tracing it over the wet paper.

"There's Santa Barbara, and this is about where we are now. But this line runs in toward the land—look, right to the coastline—where there's absolutely nothing! Not a port, not a village, not so much as a house! It's just an open beach with the jungle behind it. Now why on earth should a ship want to go there?"

Pickering, whose sharp eyes were famous aboard the *Hope-*

well, peered more closely and exclaimed, "Wait a minute—there's some writing. Look, against that mark, almost on the coastline—a cross with a circle around it, and one word. It's —*g-a-b-a-r-r-a-s—gabarras.* What does that mean, Jumbo?"

White laughed. "I forgot to bring my Spanish dictionary with me. Sorry, I've no idea, so it doesn't help much. Anyway, it looks as though that was her destination, though why—— Hey, what's that?"

It was a noise as though a thousand hammers had suddenly commenced a tattoo on the deck above; and with it, merging with it and deadening it, was the rush and swish of water.

"Rain!" White gasped. "By golly!"

They scrambled to the companionway, but were almost drowned as soon as they put their heads into the open.

This was no ordinary rain. It was a black curtain of water. It was as though the sky and the sea and the air between had all merged into one. Gone were the horizon, the distant coastline, the *Hopewell,* gone even the sea and everything beyond the ship's rail.

While they stared, the other two came hastily from the engine room, soaked to the skin while scrambling through the skylight.

"We thought she was going!" Roberts gasped. "It sounded awful down below!"

Angus Duncan whistled. "I've seen rain on the Clyde," he said, "but this . . . och, but it beats Niagara, I'm thinking!"

White, frowning, muttered, "I suppose the launch had time to get back to the ship."

"Listen!" said Pickering suddenly, holding up his hand.

Faintly through the constant drumming of the rain came another sound—a deep angry bellow.

"The *Hopewell's* whistle," said White. "I've heard it too often not to know it now."

They heard it again, very faintly—and once more. Then there was only the noise of the rain.

White said grimly, "It was going away from us. The skipper's taking the ship out of our way for safety. I suppose it means he's taken the launch on board."

They felt suddenly alone. Their own ship had left them. They were aboard one which might sink at any moment. They had no boat—for the only one the *Empresa* had possessed was hanging smashed in its davits. They had not even the means of making a serviceable raft.

Angus Duncan brought their spirits down to zero. "Aye," he said slowly, "and I'm thinking we'll no be easy to find again."

It was true. The little ship had been difficult enough to see in daylight. Now the light was fading. Even if the rain lasted only an hour, pitch darkness would soon follow.

How long would they have to remain aboard the derelict? How long would she remain afloat? Supposing the rain continued for twenty-four hours or more, as these storms did at times?

White jerked them back to their senses. "It's no use moaning! No use sitting still and waiting, either. Angus, what about those pumps? Can we do anything to make sure she'll stay afloat? That's the most important thing."

The engineer pulled himself together. "Aye, ye're right. Okay, Skipper, it's only a matter of drying things out, and I've got a blowlamp working. Come on, Slim, my wee laddie. Down to the bathroom again!"

Pickering grinned cheerfully and gave White a mock salute. "Orders, sir? Shall I get a bucket and dip some of the water out?"

White flipped a big hand at him and missed. "No. See if you can find any distress flares or anything of that kind. If the *Hopewell* comes looking for us, or any other ship, we might need some in a hurry. We haven't any lights, don't forget."

They searched about, using their flashlights, and presently found a watertight box of rockets and flares.

"Right, we'll keep them handy in the wheelhouse. No sense in wasting them in this rain. I should feel happier if we could

find some oil lamps, but I suppose they're under water somewhere. I wonder how Angus . . ."

He stopped and listened. From below was coming a muffled
muttering sound.

A grin spread over White's face. "That's it!" he cried. "Oh,
good lad—he's got the auxiliary diesel running! Keep a lookout
for a few minutes, Pickles. I'm going down below."

Angus Duncan with justifiable pride showed him the little
diesel engine running. "She's a beauty!" he said. "It's just a
matter of keeping the pump suctions clear now. There's such
a muck of weed and grass in the water, d'ye see?"

That was true. The hurricane had littered the sea with weed
torn loose from the bottom and vegetation hurled from the land.
All day the *Hopewell* had been steaming through the debris that
included whole branches of trees. The flashlights showed it
floating about in the engine room.

The engineer shone his flashlight on the ship's main diesel
engine. "That's no so bad, either," he said. "Mebbe if it's only a
matter o' drying out a wee drappie water . . ."

White laughed. "Take it easy, Angus! If we can keep the ship
afloat it'll be enough for the time being. I should like some
lights, though. Any hope of getting a dynamo working?"

Angus shook his head. "Ye might as well ask for television!
When a dynamo's been soaked to its marrow it takes a power
of drying out."

White sighed. "I was afraid of that. Great codfish! What's
that crawling about in the bilges?"

It was Roberts. Soaked in oil and water, he came out clutch-
ing an armful of seaweed and other rubbish.

"Me—the *Hopewell's* smartest cadet!" he complained bitterly.
"Me, the pride of the fleet and the hope of the London office,
wearing my last clean white shirt. . . . By the way, Angus, it's
my opinion we're pumping water in instead of out. I've just
been looking at the valves . . ."

They gaped at him. Angus Duncan, looking at the level of the water by the main engine, shouted, "By hookey, you're right!"

He scrambled down among the valves and suddenly began turning wheels frantically. White, holding a flashlight for him, tried to follow what he was doing.

"You don't mean the main seacocks were open?"

"Aye," said Angus grimly, climbing back to the grating above the level of the water. "I ought to be shot for not looking, but I took it for granted they'd be closed and the outlets open. It just goes to show——"

"But why?" White cried. "They must have been trying to pump the water out before they abandoned ship. They couldn't have done that with the main inlet cocks open, could they?"

"No," said the engineer, "they could not. Ye have to reverse the circuit. Look." He shone his flashlight on the valves. "Ye close that one and open this, and that brings the water this side o' the pump. . . ."

It was complicated, but obvious once it was explained.

"Do you think they made the same mistake?" White asked. "Were they pumping water in all the time?"

Angus shook his head. "Impossible. Look how much the water came up in those few minutes! Och, but it's just as well yon Slim noticed it!"

"Then—someone reversed the valves just before they abandoned ship. Is that what you mean?"

"Aye, that's about it. Left the auxiliary engine running, I shouldn't wonder."

"But why didn't the ship sink?"

The engineer shrugged. "The inlets choked with weed and the engine stopped. Ye saw what Slim brought up just now. We've taken tons out like that already."

"But why? It's crazy! You pump the ship out until you decide to leave her, and then pump her full? It doesn't make sense!"

"It would," said Angus quietly, "if you *wanted* the ship to sink after you'd left her."

"You mean—for the insurance money, or something like that? But she's a new ship and full of cargo! I've heard of old wrecks being over-insured and thrown away—not lately, but it used to happen before Lloyd's got wise to it. But to do it with a ship like this is just mad!"

"Maybe they didn't want her remaining afloat and becoming a danger to navigation," Roberts suggested.

"Um . . ." White murmured doubtfully. "Not many men would think of that, abandoning ship in a hurricane."

"Not many would think of reversing the pumps, either," said Angus. "There was a powerful reason somewhere, I'm thinking."

And there they had to leave it for the time being. White returned to the deck, where Pickering greeted him with a new problem.

"I've been looking at the chart again. Did you notice how that current runs? It wouldn't surprise me if we drifted ashore during the night!"

White groaned. "Always the cheerful little angel! We'd better take a cast of the lead, I suppose. Didn't I see a lead line somewhere?"

"On a reel aft," said Pickering. "It was a machine once, but I suppose the sea smashed it. The reel is wedged in between those two broken ventilators."

They went out into the drenching rain together. The rain filled their eyes and ears and nostrils. Oilskins were useless against it, and had long since been cast off.

Pickering held the flashlight while White dropped the lead over the side and ran out line. The line fell slack as the lead touched bottom, and White read off the marking.

"Eighteen fathoms! I reckon we're drifting in all the time! I'm certain we had more water than that under us before we left the *Hopewell*. Let's look at the chart again."

Water poured from them as they bent over the chart. White mopped it from the paper with a damp towel from the captain's cabin.

"Oh, confound the rain! Look—there's eighteen fathoms marked, only about three miles off shore! We were at least six miles off a couple of hours ago, I'm sure. Well, we can't do anything about it. If we go ashore, we do. It's a soft beach, thank goodness, and there's no wind."

"Couldn't we drop the anchor?"

"Um. . . . Well, we won't—yet. We'll get another cast of the lead in half an hour or so and see where we are then."

"I say, Jumbo, there's another thing!"

"Oh, no! What?"

"I've found the skipper's private grub store. Are you hungry?"

White stared at him. Then he roared with laughter. "That's a relief! I thought you were going to report another calamity! What is it—a can of fancy biscuits?"

"Not likely! Cans, mostly—but there's ham, chicken, sardines, fruit, cream, asparagus, beans, spaghetti, olives, garlic. . . . It's in a little pantry affair just off the messroom. There's a sort of pressure cooker—worked by kerosene, I think—and a refrigerator—only that isn't working—and a fresh-water pump which *does* work."

"Pickles," said White solemnly, "you're a genius. Yes, I am hungry. I hadn't realized it before. Attaboy! We'll eat like Spanish captains for once! I'll give the *maquinistas* a shout."

It was a strange feast—a strange mixture of luxury foods served from cans and eaten by the light of flashlights. The rain poured through a smashed skylight onto the messroom floor, and they themselves formed puddles of water where they sat. But hot coffee, produced by Pickering somehow from the kerosene cooker, washed the meal down and gave them a comfortable feeling inside.

They discussed the twin mysteries of the little ship—why she

was bound for an empty stretch of coastline and why her seacocks had been left open. They talked of the possibilities of being
found in the morning—for by now they were resigned to spending the night on board.

"The *Hopewell* is bound to have reported the affair by now,"
White said. "I'll bet the wireless was buzzing almost before we
heard her whistle blowing. So even if she doesn't find us in the
morning someone else will. The only trouble is, we'll probably
be stranded on the beach by then. It'll mean some wretched tug-
boat will come along and tow the ship off, and get all the salvage
money, and our efforts will be wasted!"

"Hurr-umph!" said Angus Duncan.

"Urr-hum!" said Roberts.

"And what," inquired White sarcastically, "does all that mean?
Or have you both contracted bilge water in the throat?"

Angus Duncan smiled his slow smile. "Aye—and, as they say
in bonnie Scotland, mebbe och aye! In other words, laddie, if a
wee bittie diesel can be made to work, so mebbe can a big one."

"You mean the main engine? Gosh, if you could . . ."

Roberts expanded his chest. "Well, we're not promising—
are we, Angus? But if they were to give us half their salvage
money we might."

"All right," said Pickering happily. "My share was to be
fourpence, wasn't it? So if I promise to give you tuppence . . ."

Angus laughed and prodded Roberts to his feet. "Awa' down
below, laddie. There's work to do—and we'll have cold chicken
and hot coffee at midnight, Skipper, if it's no trouble to you."

"None at all!" White laughed. "Do you prefer it with garlic
or without?"

A few minutes later he was not quite so cheerful, however.
Another cast of the lead showed that they had drifted still nearer
to the coast. The depth of water was only twelve fathoms.

But, to counteract that, the auxiliary diesel was still chugging
steadily, and the level of the water within the ship had gone

down considerably. The main deck, from being almost flush with the sea, was now a clear foot above it.

To pass the time they hoisted the broken mast on board. It was only a light signal mast, after all, but it would be in the way if they did get the ship moving. They found a tarpaulin and rigged that as a cover over the engine room skylight to keep the rain out, and a smaller one over the messroom skylight. That made the ship seem more comfortable, somehow.

At eleven o'clock a cast of the lead showed eight fathoms of water. At midnight the measurement was only six fathoms. White began to chew his nails. Time was running very short. He imagined he could hear surf beating on the beach—but perhaps it was really the thunder of the rain.

And then, abruptly, he knew that there was a new noise—but it came from the engine room. Not the main engine, certainly, but perhaps an air compressor. . . .

He ran to the skylight. Just as he was about to lower himself through it there came a cough, a splutter, a roar. The main engine had burst into life!

He shouted madly. "Cheers! Oh, nice work! Oh boy, oh boy, that's the stuff!"

For a moment he saw Angus's face, black with oil, grinning up at him. Then he left the skylight and ran back to the wheelhouse.

Pickering was already turning the spokes of the wheel, laughing excitedly. "We're moving!" he crowed. "We ain't a broken-down old wreck any more! Hey—what's the matter, Skipper?"

White had knocked him away from the wheel. He was turning the spokes desperately. "Idiot! You're heading south! Look at the compass! She's heading straight for the beach!"

Slowly—agonizingly slowly—the little black line in the compass bowl which showed the direction of the ship's head moved against the compass card. It swung to south-southwest—to southwest—on to west and past it.

At northwest White spun the wheel back and steadied the ship. "All right. That'll do for now. Keep her on northwest, Pickles."

A little chastened, Pickering took the wheel again. But he soon cheered up. Oh, this was marvelous! Why, the ship was alive!

But now another problem arose. Where was the *Hopewell?* Would she be in the same area still—and where was that? The *Empresa* had drifted miles inshore. Now she was steaming out. But what exactly was her position? No one could say.

The four of them discussed the matter, with the engine shut down to a crawl and for the moment taking care of itself. The rain had definitely eased now, but the sky was still black and the night like ink.

"I vote we head straight for Santa Barbara," Pickering said with enthusiasm. "Golly, if only we could take her into port under her own steam!"

But White was worried. Supposing the *Hopewell* spent hours —perhaps all the next day—in searching for her lost derelict?

Eventually he came to a decision, which the others did not question because he was in command. "I'll tell you what—we'll jog along here, just keeping off the coast, till daylight. If we don't see her then, we'll go full out for Santa Barbara. I don't trust the weather, and I certainly don't want to be caught out in another hurricane!"

They accepted that and took turns to snatch an hour's sleep— Roberts occupying the captain's sodden bunk because, he said, it gave him a nice feeling of importance.

At length a gray dawn came, reminding them more of the North Sea than the Caribbean. The clouds were heavy, the atmosphere hot and humid, the horizon misty.

They could see the coast, a faint gray line to the south, but nothing else. Not so much as a wisp of smoke indicated the position of the *Hopewell* or any other ship.

"All right," said White quietly. "Full ahead, Angus. Steer

west, Pickles. We'll follow the coast along until we sight Cape Mala. That'll give us a lead into Santa Barbara."

The others did not take his decision so quietly. Angus uttered a Highland skirl as he vaulted over the engine room skylight. Pickering whooped as he seized the wheel. Roberts beamed joyfully as he suggested, "I say, Jumbo—aren't we entitled to *all* the salvage money if we take her into port? I don't see that the *Hopewell* will deserve any!"

"Shylock!" said White scornfully. "By Jove, when you're in distress it'll serve you right if you don't get rescued at all!"

And at that moment—before the main engine had even worked up to full speed—Pickering shouted, "Something coming up ahead—fast! Just look at it!"

They had little time to look. A tiny gray shape which had materialized suddenly out of the misty horizon became a slender hull, racing head-on toward them behind a foaming bow wave. The drone of powerful motors increased to a roar.

"Motor torpedo boat!" White exclaimed. "By Jove, she must be doing thirty knots! I'll bet it's the search party come out to look for us!"

He yelled down the engine room skylight. "Stop her again, Angus! The blessed Republican Navy has arrived!"

Angus came up to the skylight and gazed at the little naval craft with disapproval. "Aye," he said, "but we can do without their help, and so you'd better tell them. I've just stopped the auxiliary. She's pumped dry."

The torpedo boat wheeled around smartly; its propellers churned astern and stopped. By a superb piece of seamanship which the *Empresa's* temporary crew could only marvel at, the two vessels came together without so much as a bump, and dusky-skinned naval men dropped ropes over the *Empresa's* mooring bitts.

"By Jove," White murmured admiringly, "he can certainly handle her!"

He was a young naval officer who now abandoned his tiny bridge and sprang aboard the *Empresa,* followed by several of his men.

"Buenos dias!" he cried. "We come to ze rescue—no? We come like ze wind when we hear ze radio message!"

White smiled. "Thanks," he said, "but—we don't want to be rescued. We're taking this ship to Santa Barbara under her own power."

It took quite a lot of explaining, and the young officer was disappointed. Here they had come "like ze wind"—and they were not wanted! But at least he could show them the way to Santa Barbara. Without a chart it would be difficult. . . .

"Oh, we have a chart," White said—and then suddenly remembered the mystery attached to it.

"Get it, Pickles," he commanded, and asked the naval officer, "What are *gabarras?*"

The officer frowned. *"Gabarras* is *barcazas.* How you say him? *Barges!"*

"Barges!" White exclaimed, and began to understand. "Then the ship was going into the coast to discharge her cargo into barges. Well, that makes a little more sense. But here—just take a look at this!"

He showed the officer the chart. "You see, this was her course line, leading straight into the coast."

"And dinna forget that wee matter o' the seacocks, while ye're about it," put in Angus.

White told the officer about that, too. "I suppose the crew will be able to explain," he said. "Have they arrived in Santa Barbara? Where was the American ship taking them?"

The officer shrugged. "Possibly New Orleans—perhaps Havana. I do not know."

"Oh. Well, the cargo was certainly intended for your country, and we wondered. . . . It's a bit fantastic, I suppose, but we wondered if it was contraband of some sort. I mean, they seemed mighty anxious nobody else would find it after they'd abandoned the ship."

"*Contrabando . . .*" the officer muttered; and then he said abruptly, "I see ze cargo. *Hombres!*"

The sailors who had followed him on board jerked to attention. He rattled a string of orders at them. They ran to the main hatch and began to open it. Soon the cargo was revealed—big wooden crates filling the hold as high as the deck beams.

More orders rattled, and the sailors attacked one of the cases with the steel bars used for securing the hatch covers. Timber splintered. Wire strappings screamed and broke. Packing materials—shavings and sacking—were hurled on deck.

Then one of the men gave a shout of triumph and pulled from the shattered case—a rifle.

The other men dug like terriers after bones, and soon they were all displaying similar trophies.

They were not new rifles. Even the cadets, gaping at their astonishing cargo, could see that. The barrels showed signs of rust and the butts were smooth from much use.

"Surplus war materials," Angus Duncan muttered, "that's what they were sold as, I'll bet. Och, but there's many a newspaper man would pay big money to be seeing this!"

The naval officer seized the blurred chart suddenly. "I go here!" he exclaimed, tapping the chart where the word *gabarras* was written. "Zis ship is *arresto*—you understand? She is *contrabando*. You go to Santa Barbara *immediatamente!* I take zis chart—I give you anozzer. Also I leave you four—five—men for *guarda*."

White sighed. "Oh, well . . . We don't need them, though. We don't want to run away with the blessed rifles!"

The officer waved that aside and barked orders at his men. They closed the hatch after a fashion and then returned to their own ship, but four others replaced them immediately, bringing rifles with fixed bayonets. They stood by the hatch, glaring at

White approached the Silent Service by the cargo hatch cautiously. . . . "Mangé," he said, "you quere mangé?"

the cadets as though daring them to touch the cargo beneath.

As Roberts grumbled explosively later when the torpedo boat had gone roaring off toward the coast and the *Empresa* was surging westward, "Anyone'd think *we* were under arrest! And what happens about our salvage money now? That's what I want to know!"

Pickering, however, had a more immediate problem. "I say, Jumbo, what about breakfast? Have we got to feed the Navy, too?"

It certainly was a problem. Would the Navy appreciate sardines, canned fruit and coffee for breakfast? What had the *Empresa's* original crew lived on? Perhaps somewhere in the stores forward, which had been completely flooded, there might be ordinary things like flour and potatoes and mutton which ought to be rescued.

White approached the Silent Service by the cargo hatch cautiously. They seemed very anxious to use those bayonets of theirs on someone!

"*Mangé,*" he said, "you *quere mangé?*"

They scowled at him.

He made a motion of eating and rubbed his stomach appreciatively. They still scowled.

He sighed and went back to Pickering. "I don't know! English, Spanish, French—it's all the same to them. We'll have ours, and perhaps that'll make them feel hungry. All right, I'll take the wheel while you rustle something up."

Fifteen minutes later the cadets—with Angus sitting on the skylight listening contentedly to the beating of the big engine down below—were feasting once more upon the late captain's luxuries. And, as White had thought, the sight of them eating caused the Navy to relax a little.

The guard stirred. They looked at one another. Abruptly one sat down on the hatch and produced something from a wallet at his belt. It looked like a strip of leather, but he began to eat it

—chewing stolidly. The others hesitated, then followed suit.

"Emergency rations," said White. "Looks like dried meat of some sort. Personally I'd sooner have canned peaches and cream!"

Then Roberts had a stroke of genius. Running down below, he returned with a huge jar of olives. Without a word he set these on the hatch by the naval men.

Immediately the atmosphere changed! The men looked, exclaimed, and dipped. They rammed olives into their mouths, chattered excitedly, and held olives up to show the boys while they beamed their thanks. *"Gracias, señor! Mil gracias!"*—A thousand thanks!

The Señor waved his hand languidly, dismissing their thanks. "Tastes differ," he said kindly. "It depends upon what you're brought up to like, I suppose. I say, Angus, have you tried asparagus dipped in condensed milk? It's good!"

Friendly relations thus established, White felt a little happier. At least they were not likely to be bayoneted now! He could turn his attention to the navigation. As it turned out, it was time he did.

Pickering—as always, Pickering saw everything first!—said suddenly, "That's land ahead!"

"Cape Mala!" cried White, staring. "We *must* have been making good time! I tell you, Angus, this little ship has got some power!"

Angus smiled. "Aye, yon's a braw wee bit o' machinery, down below. And she's not full out yet, I'm telling ye. There's plenty in reserve yet."

White examined the chart. "Port ten degrees, Pickles. We don't want to get too close. There's a nasty race around the point, and the current sets inshore."

Pickles made the necessary alteration in course, and then exclaimed, "There's a ship, too! Look—close in, against the land!"

It was difficult to see in that poor visibility, but eventually they made it out—the black hull distinct against the gray land.

"A big one," said White as they drew nearer. "She's much closer in than I'd care to be! Now I wonder. . . ."

He stared in silence for a minute or two—then suddenly stiffened. "Pickles—Angus—it's the *Hopewell!*"

It was. Within three minutes the ship was sufficiently close for there to be no doubt of it.

"Starboard twenty!" White commanded. "Angus, you'd better get down below and stand by. This looks like the end of our solo effort, lads. Prepare to receive boarders!"

But he was still puzzled. Why was the *Hopewell* so close in to land? Why did she appear to be stopped? Well, he would soon know.

The *Empresa,* surging along at a good twelve knots, turned in a wide arc and approached the *Hopewell* from ahead.

"Stop engines! Steady the helm! Don't let her get any closer, Pickles—we don't want a collision to finish with!"

He saw the chief officer on the fo'c'sle head, with the carpenter and some of the men. Was the ship about to anchor? It seemed as though they were preparing for it.

"*Hopewell* ahoy! Mr. Bradfield! It's us!"

The effect of his shout was all that could be wished. The chief officer leaped to the rail and stood gaping like a stranded fish. Men rushed from all directions. The captain on the bridge actually dropped his precious binoculars.

Nobody noticed, however, that the effect on the Navy had also been considerable. Uncertain what was happening, or what to do about it, they were toying nervously with their rifles.

They shouted explanations across the water, but it was an unsatisfactory method, and presently the captain roared through his megaphone, "I'm sending a boat across! Stand by!"

The launch appeared swiftly, in the charge of the second mate. But as it approached, the Navy went into action.

The Navy rushed to the ship's side. Four rifles were pointed at the launch. Four voices shouted—and what they shouted was obvious, though it was in Spanish. "Halt—or we fire!"

The launch halted. The second mate demanded, "What the blazes . . ."

White, greatly daring, sprang to the Navy and tried to explain.

"*Amigos!* Friends! Dash it, you idiots, that's our ship! This is our second mate—*segundo official!*"

It made no difference. Not even the friendship inspired by the olives would turn them from their purpose. One of the rifles turned in White's direction threateningly.

"It's no use, sir!" he cried despairingly to the second mate. "They're guarding the cargo—it's rifles and ammunition and goodness knows what—and they won't let you on board!"

That had to be explained, too. A whole history of their adventures was shouted down to the launch. And in return the second mate told them what had befallen the *Hopewell.*

The engines, long overdue for repairs, overworked during the hurricane and afterward, had at last gone on strike.

"It's a bearing or a coupling or something," the second mate told them. "The engineers are working like mad. We're standing by to let go anchors in case we drift in any closer, but the biggest trouble is, there's another hurricane heading this way."

And that meant—he did not need to tell the cadets—that their beloved old *Hopewell* might be wrecked. Her anchors would never hold her against a hurricane on that exposed coast. She would drag them slowly inshore, and then pound herself to pieces on the beach.

White looked at the huge bulk of the ship. She was empty, and that made her seem larger, but it also made her several thousand tons lighter.

He said suddenly, almost surprised at hearing himself saying so, "We've loads of power here—a marvelous engine, Angus says. We might try. By Jove, sir, I'm jolly sure we *could* tow you, if the skipper would let us!"

It was a startling suggestion. They all digested it in silence for a while, and Roberts muttered, "If those blessed *matelots* will let us!"

"They'll have to," said White tersely. "We won't ask them. Look here, sir—couldn't you put it to the skipper? If you could pass us a hefty rope—we could at least hold the ship off the coast."

That, perhaps, was a little more reasonable. The second mate took the launch back to the ship to consult the captain and chief officer.

Minutes passed while they waited, and while the Navy rested on its rifles and asked silent questions with its eyes. But White refused to try to answer those questions. He ignored this ridiculous obstinate Navy.

But at last there came a roar through the captain's megaphone. "White! Stand by to take a towrope! Come in astern—and pay attention to orders!"

White cheered softly and sprang to the wheel. The *Empresa* steamed around again, stopped, and began to back gently in toward the *Hopewell's* bows.

"Stop her!" came the roar from the bridge.

"Catch!" yelled a seaman from the fo'c'sle head—and a light line snaked across the *Empresa's* stern.

They caught it and began to pull. The huge towing hawser attached to the end of it began to creep down from the *Hopewell's* towering bows.

It was backbreaking work, but they managed at last to get the eye of the rope on board. Then they hauled in more of the hawser until they had enough to take around three sets of mooring bitts—for to put the whole strain of towing the big ship on to one set of bitts would have pulled the bitts out of the deck.

The chief officer shouted instructions to them from above. The captain roared others—or, more often, the same ones a little later. But once he shouted to the chief officer, "Tell those confounded boys to hurry, Mr. Bradfield! We're getting much too close for comfort!"

White, glancing past the *Hopewell*, caught a glimpse of white surf breaking on yellow sand.

Then—"All fast!" White shouted, and the chief officer shouted back, "Go ahead gently! We'll pay out a good length first. I'll let you know when the strain is coming."

The *Empresa's* screw turned. She went ahead, drawing out the rope after her till she was far enough from the *Hopewell's* bows not to be in any danger of collision.

"Making fast now!" the chief officer's voice came faintly.

The rope tightened. White signaled Angus for more revolutions. The *Empresa's* screw churned madly as she struggled to free herself from the mighty weight astern.

The Navy came to investigate, and protested violently in voluble Spanish, of which no one could understand a word.

White waved them away. "*Vamos!* I'm busy. This is a matter of life and death—*vida y muerte*—savvy?"

Whether they understood or not, they retired to chew their moustaches and fiddle with their rifles.

Could the *Empresa* do it? That was the important question— and it seemed ages before any answer came. But at last Pickering, who had thrown an empty can over the side and was watching it, reported excitedly, "We're moving! We're going ahead!" The empty tin was very slowly floating astern.

Possibly they never made more than four knots. Cape Mala seemed to hang astern of them, threateningly, for hours. But it was astern, and fading slowly into the mist, and that was all the reward they asked.

It was after they had consumed their third meal on board— as mixed and fanciful as the others—that a change occurred. The *Empresa* suddenly began to surge forward.

At the same time Pickering, who was watching over the tow-rope, yelled, "She's steaming! They've got the engines going!"

At the same time a distant hail came across the sea—"Let go towrope!"

White eased the engines and put the helm over. Then, leaving the wheel, he ran to help the others. The big rope slid out over the poop and fell with a great splash into the sea. "All gone!" they shouted together, and heard the rattle of the *Hopewell's* steam windlass as it hauled the rope in.

The *Hopewell* came steaming up and drew level. The captain's voice came from the bridge. "You'd better follow us into Santa Barbara now! Well done, everybody!"

White grinned, and waved in salute. "Follow you in?" he asked in a voice which could not be heard beyond the *Empresa*. "We'll jolly well *lead* you in!" And he signaled Angus for full speed—all the speed he could give.

In the end, however, it was neither the *Empresa* nor the *Hopewell* which led, but the Navy. For the little motor torpedo boat came roaring up astern when they were still ten miles from Santa Barbara, throttled down, and insisted on keeping station just ahead.

"Just as though *he'd* done it all!" Pickering complained. "Why, the blessed Navy hasn't done a thing yet—except wolf down a jarful of olives!"

They did not know then, but learned afterward that the little torpedo boat had in fact found a complete rebel army headquarters hidden in the jungle, near the place where *gabarras* had been marked on the chart. Though the leaders had evidently fled across the frontier after the supposed loss of their cargo of arms, sufficient evidence had been found to make sure that no further rebel activities in that quarter would be attempted.

But, as Roberts said, the real problem remained. What about their salvage money?

"We salvage the *Empresa*," he said plaintively, "but along

comes the Navy and confiscates her. Then, while she's still confiscated, she salvages the *Hopewell*. We do all the work, both times, but what are we going to get out of it? That's what I want to know!"

White said sadly, "About tuppence, I should think. That's half my original estimate, isn't it? You see, what with our owners, and the *Empresa's* owners, and the Navy and the President and Lloyd's and all, there's bound to be a whacking big lawsuit which will take at least two years to settle."

"Ah well," said Slim Roberts, "I was born poor, and I suppose I'll die the same. It's a hard life!"

What's in a Name?

In the British Royal Navy there are admirals, commodores, captains and lieutenants; in the Merchant Navy there are officially only masters and mates, though by courtesy they may be called captains and officers and a senior captain may be called commodore.

All these names are ancient, though some have acquired their present meaning only in recent times.

Back in the Middle Ages there was no British Royal Navy and no ships built especially for fighting. All ships had to be prepared for fighting sometimes, of course, because there were pirates even in the English Channel, but they fought only when necessary. Even if the king owned ships, as some kings did, they were built to carry cargo and could be hired by private merchants.

The man in charge of such a ship, who sailed and navigated her, was called her master, and to assist him he had his mate or mates.

When the king needed ships for war he hired merchant vessels and built on them fighting "castles," the forecastle and the after-

castle, which were like wooden forts. He put in them soldiers
with guns and other weapons which were normally stored in the
Tower of London, and a ship so taken was henceforth known
as "of the Tower." Thus the *Mary of Poole* would become the
Mary of the Tower.

With these ships in the king's service went the master and his
mates, the seamen, cook and carpenter, to sail them. But the
master was no longer in real command of the ship. He had to
obey the "captain" in charge of the king's soldiers—probably
a knight or nobleman. And such a captain naturally had his
lieutenants under him who also took precedence over the mere
civilian sailors.

The captain said where he wanted the ship taken, and the
master sailed her there, even putting her alongside an enemy ship
in battle—or "aboard" her as the term originally meant. But the
seamen in those days took no part in the fighting.

During Tudor and Elizabethan times ships came to be built
especially for fighting, but the old system was maintained with
regard to their crews—there was a captain and a body of soldiers
for fighting, a master and a crew of seamen for sailing the ship.
The only difference was that gradually the seamen learned how
to fight with the big guns, while the soldiers concentrated on
boarding and hand-to-hand fighting, or sniping with their muskets.

During the fighting against Spain, and especially against the
Spanish Armada, it was the English seamen-gunners who in
great measure brought England victory. Spain still depended on
soldier-gunners, who were often seasick and in any case not as
skilled in shooting from a heaving ship.

Another change was that the soldier captains of ships taught
themselves the business of seamanship. Men like Drake, Haw-
kins, Frobisher and Raleigh were soldiers and sailors too. Thus
we find Drake, who was originally only a merchant seaman,
sometimes called "Captain," sometimes "Admiral," and sometimes "General." Men of noble birth like Raleigh, Lord Howard

of Effingham, Sir Richard Grenville, were proud to be called seamen. It was Drake who put into words the spirit of the age when he said, "I must have the gentlemen to haul and draw with the mariners, and the mariners with the gentlemen."

In Stuart times, and under Cromwell, the Royal Navy came into being. The king's ships, or the nation's ships, were henceforth to be for fighting and fighting alone.

But still some of the old ways persisted. All ships carried a captain and his lieutenants, who were usually competent seamen, but they also carried a master and master's mates, whose jobs were to attend to the navigation. All through the eighteenth century, to the time of Nelson and well into the nineteenth century, there were masters and master's mates in the Royal Navy. The master was sometimes called the "sailing-master," sometimes the "pilot," and sometimes the "navigator." And so, not much more than a hundred years ago, the master eventually became the navigating lieutenant—the specialist in navigation whose advice would be sought by the captain in setting course or taking the ship from one place to another.

Captain Cook, the famous explorer, rose in the Royal Navy by way of the ranks of master's mate and master. He was sent exploring simply because he was an expert in navigation.

The term "admiral" originally meant the principal ship in a fleet or squadron. The officer in command of the fleet, who hoisted his flag aboard the "admiral," was called the general. We speak of "Admiral Blake" who defeated the Dutch in Cromwell's day, but in his own time he was called "General-at-Sea." Samuel Pepys, the great Secretary of the Navy under Charles II and James II, who is now remembered chiefly because he kept a diary, always called admirals "flagmen." They flew their flags for the time being, while they were in command of a fleet. Once ashore they were no longer "flagmen," but only captains.

Eventually the term "admiral" came to mean the man rather than the ship, but it is still applied only to the man actually doing the job and while he was doing it. It was not a permanent rank.

For many years the Royal Navy was divided into three fleets or squadrons—the Red, White and Blue. Each of these squadrons had an admiral, a vice admiral and a rear admiral. Thus there were nine admirals in the Navy and no more. Nobody could become an admiral until one of those jobs fell vacant— and normally they did not fall vacant until someone died. There was almost no such thing as a man retiring, for there were no pensions.

The result was that the Navy had thousands of captains— many more than could hope to obtain command—all waiting for one of the admirals to die. A man might be captain for forty years!

This gave rise to another term, "post-captain." He was a man who actually had a "post" or job of captain. He was one of the lucky ones obtaining command of a ship. "Post-captain" remained a rank in the Navy until the mid-nineteenth century.

Eventually the Admiralty had to settle matters by making "admiral" a rank rather than a job, so that captains could be promoted—and then retired if they were too old. Pensions were given, and such retired admirals were popularly known as "yellow" admirals—or admirals of a yellow squadron which did not in fact exist.

The term "Royal Navy" was first used by Charles II. The term "Merchant Navy" did not come into existence till after World War I, when it was awarded by King George V in recognition of the war services of merchant seamen.

In Queen Elizabeth's time the expression "Navy of England" meant every ship or boat owned by an Englishman—Queen's ships, merchant ships, fishing boats and all. There was no special term for merchant shipping until about two hundred years later, when "Mercantile Marine" came to be used, and this was the official term till "Merchant Navy" came along.

The great East India Company used the term "Merchant

Service" or "Marine Service" for its own ships and men, and "Merchant Service" was much used for merchant shipping generally until our own times.

The East India Company also called its masters and mates "captain" and "officers"—First Officer, Second Officer, and so on. These names were copied by many of the big shipping companies later, and are still used today. But officially, when a man passes his examinations and qualifies to serve in command of a merchant ship, he becomes a "master" whether his ship be a small coaster or a great liner.

The East India Company also used the term "commodore" for the senior captain when two or more ships were sailing in company, as they often did in those days for the sake of safety. In the Royal Navy "commodore" is a rank above captain and below rear admiral. In the Merchant Navy it usually means the senior captain in a particular shipping company's service.

In reality, of course, there is no such thing as a Merchant Navy or Merchant Service. Each shipping company employs its own masters and mates, or officers, promotes them or discharges them as is convenient. A man may be a captain in a liner company's service today, and tomorrow be out of work and just plain "Mr. Smith."

But since about 1850 all such masters and mates have been compelled to take examinations after a due period of service at sea, and must hold certificates of competency awarded at first by the Board of Trade and now by the Ministry of Transport. And nowadays their conditions of service, rates of pay, leave, pensions, etc., are regulated by the government.

It will be a sad day when the terms "master" and "mate" are officially abolished. They are ancient and honorable terms, and the men entitled to be called by them should be proud.

This famous ballad is frequently reprinted in anthologies about the sea, and has always been one of the author's favorite poems. It is a tribute to one of England's most dashing, bold and colorful sea adventurers.

🦋　DRAKE'S DRUM　🦋

By Sir Henry Newbolt

Drake he's in his hammock an' a thousand mile away,
   (Capten, art tha sleepin' there below?)
Slung atween the round shot in Nombre Dios Bay,
   An' dreamin' arl the time o' Plymouth Hoe.
Yarnder lumes the Island, yarnder lie the ships,
   Wi' sailor lads a dancin' heel an' toe,
An' the shore lights flashin', an the night tide dashin',
   He sees et arl so plainly as he saw et long ago.

Drake he was a Devon man, an' ruled the Devon seas,
   (Capten, art tha sleepin' there below?)
Rovin' tho' his death fell, he went wi' heart at ease,
   An' dreamin' arl the time o' Plymouth Hoe.
"Take my drum to England, hang et by the shore,
   Strike et when your powder's running low;
If the Dons sight Devon, I'll quit the port o' heaven,
   An' drum them up the Channel as we drummed them long ago."

Drake he's in his hammock till the great Armadas come,
   (Capten, art tha sleepin' there below?)
Slung atween the round shot, listenin' for the drum,
   An' dreamin' arl the time o' Plymouth Hoe.
Call him on the deep sea, call him up the Sound,
   Call him when you sail to meet the foe;
When the old trade's plyin' an' the old flag flyin',
   They shall find him ware an' wakin', as they found him long ago.

About the Author

CAPTAIN FRANK KNIGHT, popular author of seafaring tales from the days of the Vikings to the present, has successfully combined two lifelong passions: writing and the sea. His first book was written when he was ten, and at fifteen he joined the British Merchant Navy, spending the next ten years afloat in various parts of the world. In World War II he became a navigation instructor in the Royal Air Force.

It was not until after the war that Captain Knight turned again to writing, this time with years' accumulation of sea lore and experience, his own and that of his former shipmates, some of them old salts who, in their earliest years, had actually sailed on clipper ships.

Captain Knight has since published more than twenty books of sea adventure, many of them based on historical fact, and equally popular with young readers in England and America.